THE FIRST TEMPTATION
OF S. ANTHONY

(1856 ms)

(see pp. 213-4)

CONTENTS

LIST OF PLATES

LIST OF ILLUSTRATIONS IN
THE TEXT

Here come others! Behold!

THE FIRST TEMPTATION OF SAINT ANTHONY BY GUSTAVE FLAUBERT TRANSLATED BY RENÉ FRANCIS AND ILLUSTRATED IN COLOUR & BLACK AND WHITE BY JEAN DE BOSSCHÈRE ❧ ❧

PRIVATELY PRINTED FOR
RARITY PRESS, INC., NEW YORK
1932

Messer. Demons
Pray you, let me be !

Messieurs les démons
laissez-moi donc!

(p. 193)

PART I

EVENING, on a mountain; desert on the horizon; to the right hand is S. Anthony's hut; near the door is a bench; to the left is a small chapel. A lamp is hung thereto above a painting of the Blessed Virgin. ✳
In front of the hut, on the ground, are a few baskets of palm-leaves.
In a cleft of the rock lies the hermit's pig, asleep in the shade.
S. Anthony is alone, seated on the bench, busy with his baskets. He raises his head and looks at the sun.

S. ANTHONY. Enough have I laboured so. Let us to prayer. [He moves towards the chapel, then pauses.] Yet a little and it will be the hour. When the shadow of the cross shall touch yonder stone, then will I begin my prayers.
  [He paces slowly up and down, his arms hanging loose.]
The sky paleth. The gier eagle wheeleth hither and thither, the palm-trees shiver, anon will the moon rise,

3

✳ p. 194

. . . and to-morrow? the sun will return! then will he set. And ever thus, ever. I, I shall awake, I shall pray, I shall finish these baskets that I deliver unto the shepherds that they may bring me bread. Then shall I pray, shall I awaken, . . . and ever thus, ever. . .

[He sighs.]

Ah God! do the rivers weary them of the flow of their waters? Doth the sea tire of beating upon her shores? Have the trees that writhe in the great winds no longing to depart with the birds that raze their topmost boughs? [He looks at the shadow of the cross.] Yet the breadth of two sandals, and it will be the hour for prayer; it must be so.

[A tortoise crawls out from between the rocks, S. Anthony looks at it.]

Of a truth the beast is most fair to look upon.

[He then drowses.]

I am greatly wearied to-night. My hair-shirt doth irk me; how heavy it is!

[He turns round and perceives the shadow of the cross; it is past the rock.]

Ah! woe on me! what have I done? up, up, make speed!

[He strikes two pebbles together and kindles a dry leaf and lights the little lamp, which he then hangs up again on the wall; the night is almost fully come; he kneels down.]

There be they that pray for this alone that it pleaseth them to pray, that humble them for the sake of lowliness; but I? is it for need or for duty? enough, enough, away with these thoughts.

Hail, Mary, fulfilled of grace. How greatly do I love Thee! wherefore might I not have walked in the dust of the roadway, and followed Thy long floating blue veil what time, to the measured pace of the ass whereon Thou didst fare, it rose behind Thee and disappeared under the plane-trees.

S. Anthony

[He breaks off; the tortoise moves forward, the
    pig wakes up.]
Ah! the face of Her! it is as though I had never beheld
it! I would it were larger.
A VOICE. [Murmuring, almost inaudible.]
Raised up on high, so wouldest thou?
S. ANTHONY. [Starts.] Who speaketh? [He listens.]
Nay, it was my thought.
THE VOICE. [Again.] Raised up on high, graven out-
ward even as an image that thou mightest seize it with
thine hands.
S. ANTHONY. Art Thou not the Beloved of them
that know no love?
THE VOICE. Pray unto Her, Anthony, and She shall
love thee; lo, She maketh sign unto thee.
                                    [The picture shakes.]
S. ANTHONY. Nay! She moved; peradventure it
was the wind.
THE VOICE. Ay, the wind of the evening that bloweth
from the hot seas.
S. ANTHONY. Accursed be it if it soften the heart of
the solitary!
THE VOICE. What? art thou not humble, art thou
not pure, art thou not strong?
S. ANTHONY. I?
THE VOICE. Ay, thou. Thou hast despised all joys,
all feasting, all women, the sound of the chariots and
the praises of the multitude.
S. ANTHONY. [Smiling.] It is truth; naught that
tempted other men hath beguiled me.
                        [He sets him again to prayer.]
THE PIG. I behold my lusty body in the pools as it were
in a mirror; I delight to look upon myself. My paws are
lean, mine ears are long, mine eyes are small, my belly is fat.
THE VOICE. [Stronger.] Noah was drunk with wine,
Jacob lied, Moses doubted, Solomon was found wanting,
Peter denied, but thou? . . .

*) p. 194

S. ANTHONY. Wherewithal should I be drunken? To whom should I lie? Did I doubt, then should I not be here; less than any other have I failed; never have I denied the Lord.

THE PIG. In very truth I see no beast created that exceedeth mine own self in worth.

[Vague shadows appear deep down in the scene; whisperings are heard; the wind blows, the lamp sways.]

S. ANTHONY. [Resuming his prayers.] Blessed art Thou among all women.

THE VOICE. [Repeats.] All women.

S. ANTHONY. May Thy name . . .

THE VOICE. Softer than a kiss, sorrowful as a sigh. . . .

S. ANTHONY. Mary, Mary.

THE VOICE. See Her delicate eyelashes that lower, Her hands white as altar candles; Her eyes roll, Her lips tremble.

[A gust of wind tears off the picture of the Blessed Virgin, who rises up, tall as a living woman.]

S. ANTHONY. Lo! Lo! She waxeth great! what is this aileth me?

THE VOICE. Nought. It is a woman.

S. ANTHONY. [Striking his brow.] The thought of it!

THE VOICE. See.

S. ANTHONY. Lo! She casteth back Her head; Her loins writhe.

THE VOICE. Ay, and Her locks fly forth. . . . Ah! the long locks, the locks of gold! breathe in their sweetness, kiss them!

S. ANTHONY. Enough! enough! In the name of the Lord depart, thou vision of hell!

[All disappears. The pig groans. S. Anthony gazes into the distance melancholy.]

(VARIANT: *Note: The* 1856 *MS. contains
the following variant, on a page gummed
to p.* 5.)

THE VOICE. [Resumes.] One night—it was at the
City of the Sun, on the Nile—thou didst watch, even as
now, hearkening to the clear fall into the porphyry
basons of the fountains that the lions blew from out
their nostrils; two torches there were, two torches at
a bed-head, and nigh the bed myrrh smoked in a brazen
tripod. A long veil stretched out covered a slender
shape, and the middle thereof was hollow—even as
the soft curve of a wave that giveth place; it swelled
gently towards the head thereof, and the straight folds
of it flowed down on either side even unto the ground;
that was the daughter of Martiallus the quaestor, dead
that same morn, the morrow of her wedding day.
As thine eyes passed to and fro upon her, it seemed
unto thee now and then that the cloth trembled from
one end even to the other, and thou didst step three
paces forward to look upon her face, thou liftedst the veil.
The funeral wreath was knotted tightly; it girt her
ivory forehead; her eyeballs waned in the milky colour
of her hollow eyes. She seemed to sleep; her mouth
was open, for her tongue passed over the edge of her
teeth.
And thou saidst unto thyself: but yesterday she was
alive, she spake, her arms had held him therein, her
unmoving heart had beaten; the very walls still held
in their angles the oppression of yesternight and the
broken speech thereof.
Thou didst approach, thou didst bow thee above her;
upon the right side of her neck was a red spot; thou
didst divine it.
Aha! In a myrtle bush the lark cried aloud; the boat-
men upon the river took up their song again, and thou
didst betake thee once more to prayer.

*) p. 194

S. ANTHONY.   Ay, ay.   I remember.

THE VOICE.   The nipples of her breast lifted up her gown.

S. ANTHONY.   Yea, and the gold ring on her finger, stricken by the light of one of the torches, it sent forth a great ray.   Just such a night as this it was; the air was heavy, my breast failed me.

[End of Variant.]

THE VOICE.   [Resumes.]   Yonder, in the sand, the purple litter doth approach, swaying softly on the black arms of the eunuchs.   Within it is the daughter of the consuls, sighing for weariness beneath the great pine-trees of her houses, there is the Lydian woman, worn with weariness, nor hath she desire any more for Adonis; there is the daughter of Judah, disquieted, seeking for her Messias.

S. ANTHONY.   [Slowly.]   Yea.   They are sick.

THE VOICE.   They are come to tell thee of their sufferings.   Some there be who die for the love of dancers, others that faint at the sound of the flutes, nor say they that it is the dancers that they love, nor is their ravishment by reason of the music.   They believe not the oracle, yet have they bent their ear at the edge of the valleys of Thessaly, they have bought of the sorcerers plates of metal that they wear upon their womb.   They deny them unto their husbands, they laugh now at the sacrifices, they are weary of all the gods, yet would they know wherefore Mary of Magdalene followed Christ over the ways.   Do not the simplest among them ask thee if it sufficeth to cherish his servant that they may please the Crucified?

S. ANTHONY.   [Greatly troubled.]   Ah! God! is the fault mine?   They came and I received them; should I not renew their life unto sinners, strengthen them that believed, convert the idolatrous women?

THE VOICE.   Nay, wherefore couldest thou not follow

the idolatress in the great hall, and kneel down by the side of her that believed on the cool stones of the sanctuary? But the sinner, the sinner shouldest thou not have forsaken, O Anthony. Little by little wouldest thou have weaned her of men, thou wouldest have taken from off her forehead the purple bands, and snatched from off her breast the prideful necklace, and drawn from off her fingers the heavy rings.

S. ANTHONY. [Wrathful.] Let her pray, let her weep, let her fast, for her the hair-shirt, the thorns!

THE VOICE. She assayeth it, she shutteth her in; lo, she is alone, she hath cast off her raiment, she untieth her shoe-latchet, the hanging urn swayeth shadows upon the whiteness of her naked side. But she dareth not yet, she shuddereth; she taketh the little chain with the barbed points, the blood starteth forth, her eyes grow pale, she swooneth away.

[S. Anthony sighs and stretches out his arms; the pig rubs his belly against the ground. The shapes hardly visible hitherto now begin to grow greater; they are the Seven Deadly Sins—Envy, Avarice, Lust, Anger, Greed, Sloth, Pride. There is an eighth figure, smaller than these—Logic. They hover, like shadows, lightly, all round S. Anthony, and the outline of them is cast forward on to the rocks.]

S. ANTHONY. [Looking at his pig.] What herb hath he eaten that he slavereth in that wise? Yet thou art wont to seem happy, and every morning, when I awaken . . .

ENVY. Others, at that same hour, hear the laughter of children.

S. ANTHONY. [Sighing.] Ay, of a truth!

ENVY. The ants have their brood. On the surface of the waters the dolphins swim together, the male with the female. Hast thou seen the wandering she-wolves that gallop in the forest, bearing their young in their jaws?

S. ANTHONY. But I—I am more solitary than the
wild beasts in the woods or the monsters underneath
the sea.
LOGIC. Who desired it ? Who constraineth thee ?
ENVY. Thou sufferest, thou art athirst. Others even
now lie upon ivory beds and eat snow in silver saucers.
S. ANTHONY. Yea. Indeed, so is it.
AVARICE. Hadst thou not given thy goods to the
poor . . .

LOGIC.

GREED. Thou wouldst have cellars full.
IDLENESS. And thou wouldest sleep stretched out
upon the fleeces of thy flocks.   [Silence.]
ENVY. [Resumes.] Why didst thou not buy the charge
of a tax-gatherer at the gate of some bridge ? Then
wouldst thou have seen, now and then, wayfarers who
would have told thee new tidings . . . strangers in
curious vesture, soldiers who love laughter.
AVARICE. Thou wouldest have shaped holy images,
to sell them unto pilgrims, and thou wouldest have

stored the price thereof in a jar, and buried it in the ground, within thy hut.

S. ANTHONY. Nay. Nay. Never.

ANGER. Thou shouldest have had an heavy sword beating against thy bare leg. Then wouldest thou have passed through the dark forests with thy stout comrades; thou wouldest have pitched upon the heath and drunk of the waters of strange lands.

S. ANTHONY. Nay. Nay.

PRIDE. Had not the pride of thy merit cast thee into the ignorance that shutteth thee in, thou wouldest be this day a wise man, a doctor, a master!

LOGIC. Thou wouldest know the cause of eclipses and of sicknesses, the virtue of plants, the reckoning of the stars, the earth, the heavens.

PRIDE. Kings, curious for speech of thee, would make thee sit by their side.

AVARICE. Ay, and they would send thee away laden with great gifts that men would pack in chests.

[Silence.]

LOGIC. [Resumes.] Who hindered thee from being a priest?

PRIDE. Canst thou dream of the unspeakable joy that with words thou canst cause the Most High to come down from Heaven?

LUST. Ay, and shake the hearts of fearful women as it were the wind?

ENVY. Get thee back unto Alexandria, preach unto the converts, make oration in the Councils. . . . Why shouldest not thou, even as any other, be a bishop?

S. ANTHONY. Nay, but the sight of those great followings would affright me—I who at times feel within mine heart infinite doubt to discern what is just.

LOGIC. Ay, so thou sinnest often for lack of counsel.

IDLENESS. Better to have remained among the holy men.

LOGIC. In such wise should a man live happily, be fat and well-liking, and saintly.

S. ANTHONY. [Sighing.] Ay, indeed.

THE SINS. [Repeating, one after the other.] Ay, indeed, indeed.

LOGIC. Bethink thee of thy life as it now is.

S. ANTHONY. Ay, well I know it. Rather is it a death-bed. Howbeit, at times I have had lights of blessedness wherein it seemed unto me . . .

LOGIC. [Interrupting him.] Nay, thy memory leadeth thee astray. For happiness, when a man shall turn his head to see it once again, doth bathe its summit in a vapour of gold and seemeth to attain unto the heavens even as the mountains who lengthen their shadows unto the twilight, yet are they none the higher thereby.

S. ANTHONY. [Begins to weep quietly.] Alas, alas! Even as one who would sleep, but lice torment him who passeth his hands about his face, who groaneth and sobbeth, awakened continually in the bosom of the darkness—even so am I aware of somewhat that I may not grasp nor count, that runneth, that returneth, that burneth me, angering me, itching, devouring me. What shall I do, O Lord? whither shall I fly, or where shall I abide? Command me, O Lord. I weep even as a fool who hath been beaten, I turn at random as it were the wheel loosed from a chariot.

LOGIC. Because of thy sufferings art thou lost more and more daily.

S. ANTHONY. How?

LOGIC. On the altar men place candlesticks of gold with flowers in bloom, they shut in the bones of the martyrs beneath fine pearls and topazes. Why then dost thou refuse happiness and spread unceasingly upon thy soul as it were a pall of mourning nor thinkest thou that the heel of God is upon it?

S. ANTHONY. [Abashed.] Is then penance of none avail?

SOMEWHAT THAT I MAY NOT GRASP NOR COUNT,
THAT RUNNETH, THAT RETURNETH

LOGIC.   Fret not thyself so greatly for works !   What matter deeds !   Before the Most High the cedars and the blades of grass are of equal stature.   Where then is the worth of thy holiness and the greatness of thy lowliness ?

S. ANTHONY.   Howbeit . . . the Law. . . .

LOGIC.   Do not the Jews say . . . the Law ?   the Sadducees who preach it, and the Pharisees who sell it ?   Came not Jesus to destroy it ?   Said He not that He was the sword ?   Hath the Law fed the multitudes, or calmed the raging waters, or flamed upon the Mount Tabor ?   The Law !   In the name of the Law were the prophets slain ;   the Law crucified Jesus, the Law stoned Stephen.   Of the Law died Peter and also Paul and all the martyrs.   The Law is the curse of the serpent, and the Son of God came to redeem the nations therefrom.   The Spirit that was aforetime once imprisoned in Israel is now freed and can be increased at His ease in His fulness.   Let Him fly toward the south and toward the north, toward the west and toward the east.   For Samaria is no longer accursed ;   nay, even Babylon hath been raised up from her sadness.

S. ANTHONY.   Lord, Lord, I feel as it were a flood arise within me.

LOGIC.   Let it rise !   It cleanseth thee.   [Silence.]

S. ANTHONY.   [Trying to collect his ideas.]   Howbeit . . . the Son was sent by the Father in order that . . .

LOGIC.   Why not the Father by the Son ?

S. ANTHONY.   He was to come after !

LOGIC.   Being created of Him without doubt ?

S. ANTHONY.   Nay.

LOGIC.   Who created the world ?

S. ANTHONY.   The Father.

LOGIC.   And where was the Son then ?
        [Opposite the Deadly Sins, behind the chapel, appear other shadows, lesser in stature and more numerous.]

And where was the Son then? Was He the Christ inasmuch as Christ was man and men were not? And the Spirit, what did He?

S. ANTHONY. They were one.

LOGIC. One! three Gods!

S. ANTHONY. Nay, they were one.

LOGIC. But inasmuch as Christ Jesus was God albeit He was man, where was God while He lived? What did God when He died? Where was God when He was dead?—for He died.

S. ANTHONY. [Making the sign of the cross.] Yea, and rose again.

LOGIC. But if He was before life was, there was no need that He should rise again, whereby He should once again have being after death. What did He with His mortal body? What befell His human soul? Did He bind it to His Godhead soul? Then would He be a man who should be God, who should be added unto God, a God who should be flesh; and inasmuch as He is but One with the Father and the Spirit, the Father and the Spirit would be flesh and all would be flesh; there would be nought but flesh?

S. ANTHONY. Nay, nay, wholly spirit.

LOGIC. Of a truth, for Christ Jesus is God. But Jesus was born, He ate, walked, slept, suffered and died; can the Spirit be born, doth He eat, doth He walk, can He die? Then did Christ Jesus suffer neither birth nor death—else was He not spirit.

S. ANTHONY. The man in Him it was that suffered.

LOGIC. Ay, not the God, of a surety! Had He been God . . .

S. ANTHONY. Nay, but He was God.

LOGIC. Then did He not suffer, He feigned suffering; He was not born of Mary, He seemed to be born. When they nailed Him upon the cross, He from on high beheld His body that men tormented. When on the third day He raised the stone of His sepulchre, it was as it were a vapour that went forth therefrom—a phantom, who shall say? Thomas doubted, who would touch His wounds; but it was easy for Him to feign wounds, inasmuch as He feigned a body; had it been a real body like unto thine, could He have passed through the walls and been borne to and fro in the firmament? Nay, if it were not a body, if it were not a man. . . . Jesus is indeed Christ? Thou dost not believe that Christ was Melchisedek nor Shem nor Theodotus nor Vespasian?

S. ANTHONY. Yea, Jesus is the Christ.

LOGIC. Ay, and the Christ is Jesus. . . . Howbeit, that He may live He must have a body, He must be, and inasmuch as He had not that body, therefore He was not, and the Christ is a lie.

S. ANTHONY. [Despairing.] Woe is me! In despite of myself hath all this entered into mine head, thought after thought. Pardon me, O Lord, pardon, how evil is it!

LOGIC. [Interrupting him.] What is evil?

S. ANTHONY. [Astonished.] That which is not good.

LOGIC. Ha! thou hast cunning discourse even as that of a Greek! Thou sayest good, evil, ill, well. Now, O wise man, evil is that which is not good, and good is doubtless that which is not evil—and after?

S. ANTHONY. [Irritated.] Nay, nay, evil is that which is forbidden by God.

LOGIC. Of a surety! of such is slaughter of men, adultery, worship of idols, theft, treason, and rebellion against the law. Therefore did He command unto Abraham that he should offer up Isaac who was his son, and unto Judith that she should slay Holofernes who was her lover, unto Jael that she should smite Sisera who was her guest within her tent; therefore commanded He unto all His people that they should make an end of all other nations, that they should slaughter beasts, and rip open the wombs of women in travail; therefore did He cause Abraham to commit fornication with Agar, and Ozeas with the harlot; therefore did Jacob steal from Laban, and Moses spoiled the king of Egypt, and David was the greatest of all robbers; therefore did the dwellers in the city rob the stranger within their gates, and the people of the Lord stole from the cities of their allies and plundered the towns they had overcome; therefore, from the days of Aaron even unto the days of Zedekias men worshipped the brazen serpent, and gave gifts unto Rahab the harlot, and rewarded the traitor of Bethel, and He, even He, sent His son who should destroy the law that He had made. If it were good, wherefore should He overthrow it? and if it were evil, wherefore did He give it? Is there aught good that is not evil or aught evil that is not good? Canst thou say that evil is, or that good is? Is there any truth? Where is untruth? The wise men have searched but have discovered nought, the prophets have spoken but have said nothing; thou shalt do even as they did, and the generations shall do even as thou doest. Tush! fret not thyself for the task, turn thou the mill of life and sing as thou toilest thereat!

S. ANTHONY. What matter to me? Do I know the counsels of God?

LOGIC. Wherefore then dost thou worship in Him what thou wouldest abhor in man, inasmuch as thou dost bow down before evil.

S. ANTHONY. Nay, all evil is in the Evil One.

LOGIC. Who then made the Evil One?

S. ANTHONY. God.

LOGIC. If the Evil One were created of God and the creation went forth from His word then was the word in Him or ever that word were spoken, and before the Evil One came into the world he was in the world, and with him was all his hell: hath he a body?

S. ANTHONY. The Evil One! a body!

LOGIC. Had he a body, he would not be everywhere at one moment, even as is God, Who, being spirit, is in all places at once. But if he be spirit then is he God, nay, rather is he a part of God. But if thou takest away a part from the whole, dost thou not destroy the whole? Wherefore, if thou dost sever from God a part of God, thou deniest God; but thou dost not deny God, thou dost worship God.

[Then Logic, in the shape of a black dwarf, clothed in parchment, with monstrous cock's spurs on his hands and feet, balancing now on one foot, now on the other, upon a rolling globe, bends down to S. Anthony's ear.]

Thou dost worship God; worship the Devil!

PRIDE. [Calling out.] Hither, my daughters!

[She appears behind the hermit. Her hair bristles, her eyes are red, her complexion pale; she is of great stature; her eyebrows are raised. A great purple cloak in which she is wrapped hides the ulcers on her legs, and she lowers her chin to look into her bosom at a serpent that is gnawing it. The sound of whistling is heard, of barking, of cymbals ringing, of little bells tinkling; and the Heresies advance, in long separate files, bearing on their heads serpents or flowers, and carrying in their hands whips, books, zodiacs, swords, idols; they wear necklaces of amulets round their necks; their faces are tattooed; they are clad in costumes of Chaldaea, Persia, and India. The faces of some are inflamed like a furnace, others are paler than shadows. There are long-bearded magicians, prophetesses with dishevelled hair, dwarfs that howl. Their breath forms a vapour in the night, and their eyes sparkle even as the eyeballs of wild cats. They crowd into a mass, climbing upon one another's shoulders; Logic, who beats the measure

c

*) see plate opposite p. 18

with a rod of iron, leads their march, and Pride laughs, strident, sneering. S. Anthony in his cell shudders. As they approach, one by one the former shadows appear in their proper shapes and mingle with the group.

First comes Lust, red-haired, white of skin, very fat, clad in a yellow gown enriched with pearls and diamonds. She is blind.

With her emerald-loaded fingers she gently lifts up her gown as far as her ankles.

Follows Greed, thin-necked, with violet lips and blue nose. Her cankered teeth droop on her chin, and her smock, stained with grease and wine, gives to her protruding belly that falls over her thighs.

Then Anger, in brazen hauberk, streaming with blood; flames spout from her vizored casque; her arms end in two leaden balls.

Then Envy, with huge ears; she pinches her lips, she gnaws her nails, she scratches her face; she lies down behind all the other Sins, wallows on the earth, and bites their heels.

Then Avarice, an old woman in re-sewn rags; she waves her right hand in the air unceasingly; it has ten fingers. With her left hand she keeps back the pieces of silver that would fall out of her pockets that are full to overflowing.

Sloth, armless and legless, drags herself painfully along the ground on her belly, sighing.

By now all the Heresies are in a confused throng. The Sins, taller than they, push them on from behind.

Brown clouds roll on to the moon that appears here and there between the rifts in them, and lights up the scene with a greenish glimmer.

The Heresies increase in number, and surround the hut; they come even to the threshold of the chapel; they soften their voices and say :]

They crowd into a mass

Wherefore tremble, good hermit? We are the selfsame thoughts with whom thou didst hold converse but a moment past; fear nought, good Anthony, fear nought.

S. ANTHONY. Ah me! the multitude of them! I fear!

THE PATRICIANISTS. For the flesh, of a surety? Ay, the flesh is evil.

S. ANTHONY. Yea.

THE PATRICIANISTS. By it we are accursed.

S. ANTHONY. Yea, of a truth.

THE PATRICIANISTS. And accursed are we by the Father of the Word, from Whom is all spirit, and Whose enemy is the flesh, even as the Evil One is His enemy. Yet, if He had created it, would He have called His handiwork accursed? Bodies make bodies, Spirit maketh Spirit; therefore hath the Devil made the body and he hath made man; Satan is the author thereof.

THE PATERNIANS. Nay, not wholly! From the breast alone even to the parts below. God hath fashioned the head wherein groweth thought and the heart wherein beateth life. But the Devil hath made the travail of the stomach and the organs of gendering and the longing of the wayfarer that goeth about in the feet.

ONE HERESY. Yea, man is of two parts so far as concerneth his body, and of one only so far as concerneth his spirit; that is to say, three parts in all. Even so God is of three parts whereof the Father is the first, the Son is the second, the Holy Spirit is the third, and the Trinity is the whole thereof.

S. ANTHONY. [Dreamily.] The whole! . . .

THE SABELLIANS. Nay! nay! Father, Son, and Spirit are one and the same person.

S. ANTHONY. [Alert.] Yea! indeed, yea! It is so.

THE SABELLIANS. They are the God-Unity. And forasmuch as the Son hath suffered Who is God, therefore have the Father and the Holy Spirit suffered Who are that same God. [They advance.]

S. ANTHONY. [Drawing back.] Nay! nay!

ALL THE HERESIES. What then is God?

S. ANTHONY. [Dreamily.] God?

AUDIUS. Of His unknown substance He hath drawn forth the worlds and the souls. He is a great spirit who hath a body.

S. ANTHONY. Leave me, leave me!

THE HERESIES. What then is the soul?

S. ANTHONY. [Dreamily.] The soul?

THE TERTULLIANISTS. It is made of flame and of air. It dwelleth in a body, it hath a place, it suffereth in hell pain beyond bearing upon the tongue. But the spirit hath neither seat nor place; it knoweth not pain nor pleasure. God alone is therefore without substance and the soul is indeed a body.

S. ANTHONY. A body! Who hath said this?

TERTULLIAN. [His cloak on his back.] I!

S. ANTHONY. Thou, illustrious Septimus, thou who didst so sternly persecute idolaters! And now art thou clothed even as one of the wise men of the Porch!

TERTULLIAN. Ay, I have written a book thereon; thou shouldest have read it.

THE HERESIES. He is an unbeliever! Shame be upon him!

TERTULLIAN. [Vanishing.] Thou deniest the master! May all light depart from thee!

THE HERESIES. [Ever pressing upon S. Anthony.] But we will not forsake thee; we abide. Who was Christ? Whence came His flesh? Was it man or God?

S. ANTHONY. God! [Correcting himself.] Nay, man!

THE HERESIES. [All together.] That is truth, that is truth!

THE APOLLINARISTS. It was the flesh of the Word and not the flesh of Mary. Should He, the Spirit, have sojourned in the womb of a woman?

THE ANTIDICOMARISTS. Wherefore not?

x) p. 196

THE MENANDRIANS, THE CORINTHIANS. Forasmuch as Christ was no more than a wise man !

ARIUS. Horror ! Desolation ! He was God the Son,
created by the Father and Creator Himself of the Holy
Spirit.

THE THEODOTISTS. He was Theodotus. There be
men that knew him.

THE SETHIANIANS. He was Shem, the son of Noah.

THAT THEY MAY UPHOLD HIM HORIZONTALLY.

THE GNOSTICS. He was the child of the Ages, the
mate of Arhamoth repentant, the Father of the Maker
of Nations who made Him who ruleth the world and
man.

[S. Anthony stands motionless, bewildered ; the
Ophites advance ; they bear an immense python,
gold-coloured with sapphire patches and black
patches. That they may uphold him horizontally,
the children raise him with straight-stretched arms,
the women clasp him to their breasts, the men

x) p. 196

press him against their bellies. They halt before
S. Anthony, and with the serpent whom they
unfold they form a great semi-circle at whose
entrance stands an old man in a white robe, thrum-
ming on a lyre; with him is a naked child playing
on the flute an air that is sweet and merry though
fully slow in measure.]

THE OPHITES. [Beginning.] He it was ! This was
known unto Moses !

S. ANTHONY. [Cries out.] Nay, nay ! how could
that be ?

THE OPHITES. Moses knew it, who raised the brazen
serpent in the wilderness.

    [S. Anthony opens his eyes, stupefied; they recom-
    mence.]

His coils are the circles of the worlds; the metals have
taken their colours from the patches on his skin; of
whatsoever he eateth nothing is rendered, he maketh
all of it to be a part of him.

Seated under a terebinth tree, she watched him rise.
His slimy body clung fast to the bark and the green
leaves were enkindled at his breath.

When he had passed through every branch he appeared
again; the bones of his jaw parted, the fruit fell.

He held it upon his teeth, and hanging by his tail to the
trunk of the great tree, he swayed his hissing head and
his ravished eyelids before the face of Eve.

She gazed eagerly upon him; he stayed him. Her
breast heaved, the tail of the serpent writhed, a lotus
flower opened, the dates of the palm-trees ripened.
She held forth her hand.

It was good, the noble fruit. She gathered up the rind
thereof to perfume her bosom.

Had they tasted more fully thereof, they would now be
gods, according to the promise of the Tempter.

Be thou worshipped, thou great black serpent, who
hast golden spots even as the sky hath stars ! Fair

serpent whom the daughters of Eve cherish, to the touch of the nail on the tightened chord, awake!; to the murmur of the hollow reed, arouse thee!; swell out thy rings!—up, up, come to our altars and lick the sacred bread that we offer unto the Lord.

> [The Ophites enclose S. Anthony in the circle of the serpent. He leaps over it with joined feet. Everything vanishes.]

S. ANTHONY. [Alone, slowly.] Therein was the most abhorred abomination that ever man could think upon! Furthermore, wherefore should the Son of God choose, among all faces, that of yonder cold beast, flat-headed, who seemeth to guard the mystery of evil within the speechlessness of his winding shape? Nay! never could He have wished that, He who was all love and sacrifice. "Take, eat," said He, "this is my body; and drink this," said He. . . .

> [A wine-skin falls at the feet of S. Anthony.]

THE ASCITES. [Drunken men and women, running round in a dance.] Hail, wine! overflow, wine! flood the world, wine! Wine is the Christ. When His side was pierced, it was wine that flowed, the wine of the Good Tidings that we honour in this goat-skin.

S. ANTHONY. [Exasperated.] Nay, the very unbelievers never committed such abominable wickedness.

THE SEVERIANS. Nay! never. Wine was born of the strength of Satan. Wine is madness, wine is lust.

THE AQUARIANS. So do we drink nought save water, which is the sign of the Word.

THE ASTOTYRITES. Accursed be the flesh, and they that use it, and they that preach it!

S. ANTHONY. Nay, but I preach it not, I use it not.

> [Applause bursts forth behind S. Anthony. He turns round and sees]

THE MANICHAEANS. [Clothed in black robes, sown with silver moons; in their ears are golden rings; they are very lean and their hair is held up by combs.]

Captive in the matter wherein it gendereth, Godhead. . . .

S. ANTHONY. [Cries out.] Nay! that cannot be!

THE MANICHAEANS. But in the Host, O Anthony, who is the Host? [He bows his head.]

Godhead assayeth to go forth from it, whereby it may be joined again unto its beginning. It escapeth from rest, from doing, from the movement of the hands and the look of the eyes, and thus flying through so many diverse occasions, there remaineth in us nought save a gross residue, the root of evil whence bodies are made. For Saclas, prince of darkness, imagined the ways of birth whereby he should enclose the least parts of Godhead; then created he two children, Adam and Eve.

But, forasmuch as the flesh constraineth God within her, let us take thought for the captivities wherein He doth languish, let us destroy in the seed of it the cause that doth crush Him. He whose loins are not proven thereto must abstain from women; rather should he draw from out himself the parts of light that be bound therein and let him take pleasure, without haste, in the delight of his loneliness. Then will his heart rejoice within him, for the thought that he hath delivered God.

S. ANTHONY. Woe is me! Meseemeth I slip, I stay not, even upon the stairs of Hell.

THE GNOSTICS. [A vast quire, composed of different groups; Saturnians, Marcosians, Valentinians, Nicolaists, Elxaites, &c. . . .] Hearken not unto those sorrowful men; they are unbelievers from Asia. Their great prophet Manes was flayed with the point of a reed, for his false pretending, and his skin was filled with straw and hung upon the gates of Ctesiphon.

We will teach thee, we who are wise and learned and pure—we will teach thee that that great God, the Eternal, Whom none may approach, Whom nought may disturb, He is not the creator of the world. Wouldest

thou know the life of Jesus before He appeared upon
earth, the exact measure of His stature, the name of
the star wherein is His throne? Here is the book of
Norra, the wife of Noah. She wrote it in the Ark, in
the night-time, seated upon the back of an elephant, by
the flame of the lightnings. Here is the book, open it!
Assay it! A line only! . . .

PRIDE. What peril is there?

S. ANTHONY. Nay, peradventure. . . .

LOGIC. It may be the thoughts that oppress thee will
flee away.

PRIDE. [Passes him the open book over his shoulder.
His eyes fall on this phrase.]

" In the beginning the Abysm was. Of His thought was
born Understanding who took Truth to wife. And of
Truth and Understanding issued the Word and Life
who begat five pairs like unto one another. Of the
Word and of Life came forth Man and the Church
who begat yet another six pairs, of whom The Comforter and Belief begat Wisdom and The Perfected.
These fifteen couples are the fifteen lesser Yokes who
are of thirty supreme Ages who are the Fulfilment or
Highest Whole, and who are God."

THE HERESIES. [Aside.] He readeth! He readeth!
He is ours!

S. ANTHONY. [Continuing.] " Barbelo, Son of Baal,
is the prince of the eighth heaven. Ialdamoth hath
made the angels, the earth and the six heavens below
him. He hath the shape of an ass."

[S. Anthony throws aside the book in a fury.]

THE GNOSTICS. [Closing in again about him.]
Wherefore? Begin again; thou hast not understood.

THE VALENTINIANS. [Tracing with their fingers
figures upon the sand.] Behold the 365 heavens that
match with the limbs of the body.

S. ANTHONY. [Closing his eyes.] I have no wish to
know them.

x) p. 196

THE BASILIDIANS. The word ABPAKAC signi-
fieth . . .

S. ANTHONY. [Stopping his ears.] I will not hear it.

THE SATURNIANS. We will tell thee the name of
the seven angels who have made . . .

S. ANTHONY. Nay! nay!

THE COLORBASIANS. The name of the seven stars
whence issueth the life of men.

S. ANTHONY. Nay! nay!

THE THERAPEUTES. Stay! stay! we shall dance
the dance of the passage of the Red Sea and sing the
hymn of the Sun.

THE RABDALISTS. [Pointing out with their wands
several points in Space.] Seest thou the Beingless, the
Universal, flowing through the hidden veins of all the
worlds as it were the blood in a great body?

S. ANTHONY. [In the midst of the Heresies.] By
what path shall I fly? Voices howl in mine ears! Where
am I? Whereon thought I? Ay! I recall it, upon
that which is the Word. What now?

    [The Heresies form a great circle around him and
    stand on tiptoe, open-mouthed.]

But I understand nought of all this. My soul is whirled
and torn in these thoughts even as the sail of a ship in
the tempest. Nay! I will no more. Back! back!

                [All vanishes. Silence.]

But Damnation standeth behind thy back, woe unto
thee! Woe! the terror of Eternity freezeth me even
unto the bowels, as it were the dark vault of a great
sepulchre.

    [Vague lamentations are heard afar off; he listens.]
Who is it that weepeth? Is it some wayfarer slain in the
mountain?

    [He picks up a trail of bindweed and kindles it at
    the little lamp of the chapel; he searches, lowering
    and raising his torch; the sounds of weeping seem
    to draw nearer.]

¹) p. 196

Ha! it is a woman.

[He sees a woman approaching; her black head-bands fall all adown her face; her torn purple smock shows her wasted arm whereon rings a coral bracelet. Under her eyes are red swellings, and on her cheeks the marks of bites, on her arms the traces of blows. She leans, weeping, on the arm of a bald-headed man who is clad in a long robe all of one red colour. He has a long grey beard; in his hand he holds a little bronze vase, which he places upon the ground.]

SIMON THE MAGICIAN. (Simon Magus.) [To Helen.] Stay thy feet.

HELEN. [Groaning on Simon's bosom.] Father, father, I am athirst.

SIMON. Thy thirst be removed from thee!

HELEN. Father, I would sleep.

SIMON. Awake!

HELEN. Ah! Father, when may I be seated?

SIMON. Stand up!

S. ANTHONY. [Bewildered.] What hath she done?

SIMON. [Calling three times.] O Understanding! Understanding! Understanding! He asketh what thou hast done; tell that thou hast to say.

HELEN. [As though awakening from a long sleep.] What I have to say, my father?

SIMON. Whence comest thou?

HELEN. [Casts her eyes in every direction round her, raises her head toward the clouds, collects herself a moment, then begins in veiled tones.]

I have memory of a far country, of a forgotten land. The peacock's tail, vast, outspread, closeth the bounds thereof, and through the spaces between the feathers ye may see a sky green as a sapphire. In the cedars the birds, whose crests are of diamond and their wings are the colour of gold, cry aloud, and their cry is as the sound of a breaking harp string. I was the light of the moon; I passed through the leaves of the trees; with my face I lit up the pale blue firmament of the summer nights.

S. ANTHONY. [To Simon, signing to him that she is mad.] Ay! I understand! some poor child whom thou hast found by chance and taken unto thee.

SIMON. [His finger on his lips.] Hush, hush!

HELEN. [Resumes.] At the prow of the galley near to the ram's head that dipped beneath the waters whensoever the waves smote it, there stood I and I moved not. The wind blew, the keel cleaved the foam. He said unto me " what matter to me if I bring disturbance upon mine own land, what though I lose my crown! thou shalt be mine, within mine house."

Menelaus wept; he aroused the dwellers in the islands; they set sail, they and their bucklers, their lances, and their horses that snorted for terror upon the decks of the ships.

How sweet was the chamber within his palace! He laid him down on purple coverings, on beds of ivory; he toyed with the ends of my tresses, he sang love songs unto me.

At eventide I went up on to the wall, I beheld the two camps and the beacons that were being kindled, Odysseus speaking with his friends at the door of his tent, Achilles fully armed driving his chariot along the shore of the sea

S. ANTHONY. But she is mad, wholly mad; wherefore then? . . .

SIMON. [His finger upon his lips.] Hush, hush!

HELEN. I was in a forest and men passed by. They took me and bound me with ropes; they bore me away upon their camels. They entered in unto me by stealth as I slept—first of all the prince, then the captains, then the men-at-arms, then the footmen who tend the asses.

They washed me in the fountain, but my blood that flowed reddened the waters, and my dusty feet troubled

One night I stood up naked, the timbrel
was in mine hand.

the spring.   They anointed me with oils, they rubbed me
with ointments, and they sold me to the folk that I might
make sport for them.

It was at Tyre of Syria, hard by the harbour, at a narrow
crossing of the ways. . . . One night I stood up naked,
the timbrel was in mine hand, I played and the Greek
sailors danced.   The rain of the tempest poured down
upon the house, the vapour of wine rose with the breath
of men and the smoke of the lamps.   On a sudden a man
entered, yet the door was not open.   He lifted his left
arm and parted two fingers.   The wind made the walls
to crack, the tripods were aflame, and I ran unto him.

SIMON.   Ay, I was seeking thee, but I found thee, I
redeemed thee.   She it is, O Anthony, whom men call
Grace, Silence, Understanding, Barbelo Mother of God.
She was the thought of the Father, the Mind that may
not be destroyed, Who created the worlds.   But the
angels, her sons, drove her from out her dominion.
Then was she the moon, she was Woman, the perfect
Agreement, the Pointed Angle.   Then, that they might
take their ease more fully in the infinite, whence they
had driven her forth, they prisoned her at the last in a
woman's shape.

She hath been Helen of the Trojans, whose memory
was cursed by the poet Stesichorus.   She hath been
Lucretia, the fair lady ravished by the kings.   She hath
been that Delilah who cut the hair of Samson.   She hath
been that daughter of the Hebrews who departed from
the tents that she might give herself unto the goats;
she it was whom the twelve tribes stoned.   She hath
loved fornication, lies, worship of idols, and folly.   She
hath abased herself in all corruption, she hath wallowed
in all wretchedness, she hath lain with all nations, she
hath sung at every cross-road and hath kissed all faces.
At Tyre she was the harlot of the thieves.   She drank
with them during the night-time and she hid the slayers
of men amid the lice of her warm bed.

I! even I! The Father unto the Samaritans, the Son unto the Jews, the Holy Spirit unto the Gentiles, I came that I should make her to arise again in her splendour, and stablish her once again in the bosom of the Father. And now, indivisible the one from the other, we go, freeing the Spirit and terrifying the Gods.

I have preached in Ephraim and in Issachar, in Samaria and in the cities, in the valley of Megiddo and on the banks of the swift river Bizor, from Zoata even unto Arnon, and beyond the mountains in Bostra and Damascus.

I am come to destroy the law of Moses, to overthrow the ordinances, to purify the impurities. I call the souls of the sons of Adam unto the greater love that they may be mad with lust or drunk with repentance. Come unto me all ye that are clothed in mire, ye that are drowned in blood, ye that are steeped in wine! By the new baptism, even as by the torch of pine-wood that men trail in the house of the leper that it may burn away from off the walls the red stains that devour them, thereby will I wash you clean even unto the bowels, even to the innermost parts of your being.

Be kindled, O fire! Leap, run, lay waste, purify, thou blood of Understanding, thou soul of Very God.

> [A white flame appears on the surface of the vase, escapes therefrom, hovers from side to side, and pursues S. Anthony.]

At the court of Nero I flew in the circus; so high flew I that none ever saw me again. My statue standeth upright in the island of the Tiber. I am Strength, Beauty, the Master! She, Understanding, is Athene. I am Apollo the god of the daylight! I am Hermes the Blue! I am Zeus the Thunderer. I am the Christ. I am the Comforter. I am the Lord. I am that which is in God. I am Very God.

S. ANTHONY.   Ah! had I holy water!

THAT DAUGHTER OF THE HEBREWS
WHO DEPARTED FROM THE TENTS

[The fire goes out. The woman utters a piercing cry and vanishes with Simon.]

S. ANTHONY. [Gasps and looks around him.] Nay !
. . . nought remaineth ! . . . ah me !

[He wipes his brow with his sleeve.]

Ah me ! How the flames ran !   [He laughs.]
Out on it ! These be vain imaginations ! The Spirit of God is not abased so low. If once the soul be yoked to evil, it ceaseth to be, say they what they will.

Yet . . . if by some mighty striving it should shake off that burden of substance that doth overwhelm it, . . . wherefore should it not rise again even unto God ? . . . then . . . then would the space of life vanish . . . and the works thereof would be of little matter.

[Thereupon appear the Elxaites, cloaked in great violet mantles, their faces hidden under masks of wild beasts.]

Believe ! What mattereth all else ! Eat of unclean meats if so be that the Spirit hungereth for the Word. Phineas bowed him down before Diana, and Peter denied Jesus ; for martyrdom is unholy and desire of suffering is a temptation of evil.

S. ANTHONY. [Repeats.] A temptation ?

[The Cainites appear ; their hair is knotted with vipers that twine round their necks and droop their heads back on their shoulders.]

THE CAINITES: Let us exalt them that are accursed, let us worship them that are abhorred ! More than Abraham and the prophets, more than Paul, and more than all the saints, they have laboured for thy soul, they have been damnéd for thee. Glory be to Cain ! Glory be to Sodom ! Glory be to Judas ! Cain begat the race of the strong, Sodom affrighted the earth by her chastisement, through Judas was it that the Son of God saved the world !

S. ANTHONY. [Slowly.] Judas ? . . . Yea, indeed, yea . . . it is so.

THE CARPOCRATIANS. [Naked down to the girdle, bearing flowers in their hands, long-haired, full-bearded, with long nails. They all have on their ears a red mark, and on their chests suns are tattooed.] Fulfil the task of the body ! This must be !

The spirit bewildered wandereth amid the chances of life, nor shall it return unto the unmoved bosom of Concupiscence until it hath fulfilled in its flesh all the works of the flesh. . . .

Come with us to the love-feasts by night. The naked women, crowned with hyacinths, eat by the light of the torches that are mirrored in the golden plates. They are free for all, as are our goods, as are our books, as is the sun, and as is God. At meat we sing songs of burial, we cut ourselves with knives, we drink the blood from our arms. We mount upon the altar. We cense ourselves with the incense from our censers.

THE FALSE PROPHETESS OF CAPPADOCIA. [Her great mass of red hair falls even to her heels. She waves a flaming pine brand, she leans with her left hand on the muzzle of a tigress who rubs herself against her thigh.] Spirit is in the flame, in the flesh, in the whirlwind. The Spirit shall leap forth for thee at the Invocation of Terror. Hearken thereunto ! I will roll thee within my love even to the depths of the abysm. Hither, hither !

> [She shakes her torch and its drops of fire fall at the feet of S. Anthony. The tigress arches her back. S. Anthony draws back, affrighted.]

S. ANTHONY. Woe, woe ! they will take me ! I fear ! The beast roareth ! How came they even unto me ! My fault it was, O God ! Have pity, have pity !

> [He gasps his scourge and whirls it rapidly round and round like a sling. The Heresies withdraw, lowering their heads between their shoulders, and with gestures of fright.]

Ah ! I was persuaded thereof ! The sign of Penitence putteth them to flight. It is thought alone that worketh evil. Away with these dreams wherein the soul doth lose itself. Deeds, deeds !

[He scourges himself, and the Montanists advance, clad in dark frocks, their heads covered with ashes, their arms folded.]

THE MONTANISTS. Courage, O Anthony ! Do as we do ; six times in a month we fast wholly, three times in a year keep we Lenten fast, every night do we scourge

THE TATIANS.

our bodies. Moreover, we baptize the dead, we veil virgins, we forbid second wedlock.

THE TATIANS. [Their heads are shaven, and they have prisoned themselves in black sacks. They cry out.]

Forbid all ! . . . the tree of Eden that bore each year twelve fruits red as blood, this, even this, is woman ! He who sleepeth in the shade thereof shall not awaken, save in hell.

S. ANTHONY. [Sorrowfully.] It is to save me from that slumber that I have sought out loneliness.

D

[The group of the Montanists opens and two women are seen advancing; they are very pale, and are clad in brown mantles. MAXIMILLA is dark, PRISCILLA is fair. They throw back their hoods and say :]

What time we dwelt in the house of our husbands we went out early in the morning without our litter, without our followers, that we might go into the taverns and corrupt the jailers. We visited the confessors, we sang psalms, we spake of angels. Our husbands the while were sore troubled in their houses. Ah! Mother of God, their kisses troubled the calm depth of faith as it were stones that one throweth into a well, the one after the other.

[St. Anthony steps forward the better to see them.] PRISCILLA. [Begins to speak.] I was in the bath, the walls streamed, the water flowed, and I drowsed to the vague murmur of the streets that rose even unto mine ears.

On a sudden I heard much clamour; men cried " He is a wizard, he is the devil! " and the multitude stayed before our house, over against the temple of Aesculapius. I rose up, unshod, and raised myself with mine hands unto the height of the casement.

On the hall of the columns of the temple stood a man robed as a freed slave, having an iron collar on his neck. He took live coals from a chafing-dish and upon his breast he drew great lines therewith, calling aloud the while " Jesus, Jesus! " The people said, " It is not permitted; let us stone him." Others praised him. But he ceased not, and when he was weary of moving his right hand he moved his left hand.

It was wondrous, mine heart was uplifted! Great open flowers turned as wheels before mine eyes, and I heard in space as it were the music of a golden bow. Mine hands loosed hold of the bars and my body fell. I know not if he had ceased to speak or if I had ceased

to hear him; but the pool of the bath was empty,
and the moon, entering, cast clear lengthening rays
upon the pavement that was strewn with blue sand.

S. ANTHONY. [Listening with attention.] Of whom
speak they?

MAXIMILLA. We were on our way back from Tarsus,
over the mountains, when we saw a man at a turning of
the road under a fig-tree.

He was plucking the leaves and casting them to the
wind.

He tore off the fruits and crushed them upon the earth.
He cried out unto us from afar, "Halt! ye!" and he
ran upon us, cursing us. The slaves hastened unto us.
He laughed aloud with great laughter. The horses
reared up, and the great hounds howled, every one of
them.

He stood up, on the edge of the precipice. The sweat
flowed upon his dark face. His black cloak flapped in
the wind of the mountains.

He called us by our names, he reproved us for the
vanity of our works and for the foulness of our bodies;
he lifted his hand in wrath toward the dromedaries by
reason of the silver bells that they bare under their
jaws. His wrath affrighted me even to mine innermost
parts; his speech was strange rapture, it was mingled
with soft winds and sweet odours; it soothed me to
sleep, it made me drunk as with wine. First the slaves
drew nigh: "Master," said they, "the beasts are
wearied"; then came the women: "The night is at
hand, we are afeared"; and the slaves departed. The
children cried aloud: "We are an-hungered"; and as
none made answer unto the women, they also departed.
But he spake on; his voice whistled, his words fell headlong; sharp-edged as daggers they made my heart bleed,
they voided it.

I was aware of one near unto me; it was my husband;
but I hearkened unto the other. He wept aloud, he

drew himself on his knees over the stones and cried out, "Thou dost forsake me!" and I made answer "Yea, get thee gone!"

> [S. Anthony opens his mouth, but Priscilla and Maximilla begin to sing.]

The Father hath dominion, the Son suffereth, the Spirit is a burning flame! The Comforter is ours! The Spirit is ours! for we are the beloved of the great Montanus!

> [They point to a black eunuch standing near them, clad in a cloak fawn-coloured with gold braid, clasped over his breast by two human bones.]

MONTANUS.   It is not Montanus whom ye love, but the Spirit of God that filleth his soul. For I am no man; that ye know, ye who faint with desire upon mine hairless breast.

Ye, my beloved, ye are Love that cannot be satisfied, forasmuch as at this present ye delight in pain, and life giveth pain unto you, as it were a running sore. Weep ye, shed tears! Let your eyes be pale even as a blue cloak that hath lost its colour in the tempest. Call upon me! I will lay you upon racks! Scourge ye the white skin of your bodies with green thistles! When the blood shall flow, then shall I come. Ay, I shall hasten . . . that I may suck it with my mouth!

> [Maximilla and Priscilla pass their arms round his waist and remain with their heads resting on his shoulder, making a sign the while to S. Anthony.]

S. ANTHONY.   In the name of Christ! In the name of the Virgin! By the excellence of all the angels. . . .

THE MONTANISTS.   Nay! thou shalt not drive us hence! Zotimus of Comanus was conquered by Maximilla, and Sotas, the bishop of Anquiala, was overcome by Priscilla. We have saints who be holier than thy saints, we have martyrs whose testimony is greater than that of thy martyrs. Knowest thou Alexander, Theodotus, Thermison? They tore out the eyes, the teeth, and the nails of Alexander of Phrygia; they rubbed his skin with honey, and upon it they cast raging wasps; they bound him with a rope to the tail of a bull that went slowly through a pasture. Thermison they tore with knives of wood; they made the blood of his entrails to flow over his face. But Satan upon a mountain-top beat Thermison during six nights with the trunk of a cedar-tree that had all its branches: then did he cast him away, as it were a stone, into the valley. Up! come! Jesus hath suffered; what is thy suffering after His?

S. ANTHONY. [Bitterly.] Nought, nought, I know it. The tears of all generations of man that would make a great sea, were they united, are but a drop of water upon a leaf before those His everlasting tears.

[Silence.]

THE MONTANISTS. [Resuming.] Love overfloweth from out the bleeding heart. The closed eyes of the ravished behold the splendours of Heaven; in the agony of the body shall the fulness of understanding come upon thee, even as the lightning that appeareth not save in the openings of the clouds.

S. ANTHONY. Yea, verily! My body doth irk me, it doth crush me, it doth choke me.

THE VALERIANS. [They are very tall, and very lean, they have daggers in their girdles and crowns of thorns on their foreheads; they seize their daggers in one hand and their crowns in the other, and they say :] Here is that shall cleave lust in sunder! Here is that shall give pain unto pride! Is it pain that thou fearest, O thou of little courage? Dost thou tremble for thy flesh, thou hypocrite? Thou liest down near unto it, thou dost watch it in its sleep; it shall awaken more ravenous than a lion. Choke thou it, cut it in pieces, make an end of it!

S. ANTHONY. I have a loathing for myself! I abhor life, and the earth, and the sun.

[Ferocious outcries burst forth and the DONATIST
CIRCONCELLIONS appear : they are filthy,
hideous, clothed in goat-skins, and they bear iron
clubs upon their shoulders.]
Accursed be the whole world !   Accursed be we ourselves !
Accursed be man !   Accursed be woman !   Accursed be

THE CLOSED EYES OF THE RAVISHED.

children !   Trample upon the fruit, trouble the spring !
Plunder the rich man who is happy, who eateth his
fill ; beat the poor man who coveteth the housing of
the ass and the meal of the dog and the nest of the

A p. 197

bird, who mourneth in his loneliness for that all men are not miserable even as he is. Feed the bears, call unto the vultures, whistle unto the crocodiles and to the lizard by the riverside!

We are the Captains of the Saints: we destroy substance whereby we may hasten the end of the world; we slay, we burn, we slaughter! We break down the dykes, we cast money abroad into the sea:

None may be saved except they suffer martyrdom; we give martyrdom unto ourselves; we flay the skin from off our feet and we run upon the shingle. We thrust spits of iron into our entrails. We roll naked in the snow.

We slay ourselves with knives, crying out, "Praise be to God!" We go up to the roofs of high houses that we may cast ourselves down headlong. We lie down under the wheels of chariots, we cast ourselves into the mouths of furnaces.

Reviled be baptism, reviled be the Bread and Wine, reviled be marriage, reviled be the anointment of the dying!

Repentance alone cleanseth the soul.

Jesus cannot be touched, Jesus cannot be eaten. Damnation upon adultery sanctified! with suffering must ye be wedded!

Damnation upon the vanity of man who must die, yet thinketh he that the flesh is eternal! Damnation upon the folly of them that hope, upon the wickedness of them that teach! Damnation upon thee! Damnation upon us! Damnation upon all, and glory be unto Death!

S. ANTHONY. Horror!

> [There is a clap of thunder; a dense smoke covers the scene; S. Anthony can no longer distinguish anything.]

Yet I dreamt not? . . . nay . . . they were there! . . . they roared round about me, and my thoughts crumbled to dust beneath their feet even as the lesser islands of sand in the rivers that fall in great masses beneath the heavy feet of the crocodiles. They spake all together and so swiftly that I could not tell their voices the one from the other. [He collects himself little by little.] Yet some there were of them who were not wholly hateful. How was this? I should have made answer unto them. I have not seen all.

[He glances vaguely from side to side, and utters a cry as he perceives in the fog two men covered with long mantles that fall even to their feet. The foremost is of great statue, of mild countenance and grave demeanour; his fair locks, severed by a parting even as those of Christ, fall in regular lines upon his shoulders. He casts down a white staff that he held in his hand, and his companion picks it up, bowing after the manner of the men of the East. This latter is clothed similarly, in a white tunic, unembroidered; he is small and fat, snub-nosed, of squat figure; he has woolly hair and is of simple aspect. Both are bare-footed and bare-headed, and covered with dust like men who have just come from a journey.]

What would ye? Speak! . . . begone!

DAMIS. [The little man.] Nay, nay, good hermit! What would I? I know not! Here is the Master. Touching our departure, charity at least should require . . .

S. ANTHONY. Nay, pardon me! Mine head is sorely troubled! . . . what is your need?—be ye seated.

[Damis sits down—the other remains standing.]

And thy master?

DAMIS. [Smiling.] Nay, he hath need of nought! He is a wise man! But for me, good hermit, I would pray thee give me a little water, for my thirst is great.

[S. Anthony fetches a crock from his cell, raises it himself, and offers Damis to drink. Little by little the smoke vanishes.]

DAMIS. [After having drunk.] Pah! how evilly it tasteth! thou shouldest have covered it with leaves!

*) p. 197

NAY, HE HATH NEED OF NOUGHT!
HE IS A WISE MAN!

S. ANTHONY. My Lord, there is not even a blade of grass at hand.

DAMIS. Hast thou nought for me to eat? My hunger is great.

[S. Anthony goes into his hut and returns with a piece of dried-up black bread. Damis bites it.]

How hard it is!

S. ANTHONY. I have none other, My Lord.

DAMIS. Ah! [He breaks the bread, tears out the crumb, and throws away the crusts. The pig makes for them: S. Anthony makes an angry gesture as if to beat him.] Nay! Suffer him! Surely all must live! [Silence.]

S. ANTHONY. [Resumes.] And ye come?

DAMIS. From afar . . . from a great distance. . . .

S. ANTHONY. And . . . ye go?

DAMIS. [Pointing to the other.] Whither his will leadeth.

S. ANTHONY. Who then is he?

DAMIS. Apollonius!

[S. Anthony makes a gesture of ignorance.]

Apollonius! [louder.] Apollonius of Tyana!

S. ANTHONY. I have never heard speak of him.

DAMIS. [In anger.] What! Never! . . . Ah! I see clearly, good man, that thou hast no knowledge whatsoever of what passeth in the world.

S. ANTHONY. Of a truth, My Lord, for my days are given over to worship.

DAMIS. Even so is it with him.

S. ANTHONY. [To himself.] With him!

[He considers Apollonius.]

Indeed, he hath the look of an holy man. . . . I would fain hold converse with him . . . it may be that I deceive myself . . . for . . .

[The smoke has vanished; the air is quite clear, the moon shines brightly.]

DAMIS. Whereon thinkest thou that thou sayest never a word?

*) p. 19) (referred to as on p. 40)

S. ANTHONY. I ponder . . . nay, it is nothing.
[Damis approaches S. Anthony and walks round him several times, stooping, nor ever raising his head;—at length—]

APOLLONIUS. [Still motionless.] What is it?

DAMIS. Master, it is a Galilean hermit who would know whence wisdom cometh.

APOLLONIUS. Let him draw nigh!

[S. Anthony hesitates.]

DAMIS. Draw nigh!

APOLLONIUS. [In a voice of thunder.] Draw nigh! Thou wouldest know who I am, what I have done, what are my thoughts; is it not so, my child?

S. ANTHONY. [Embarrassed.] If haply these things may further my salvation.

APOLLONIUS. Rejoice! I will tell them unto thee.

DAMIS. [In a low voice, to S. Anthony.] Can this be! Surely, at the first sight of thee, he hath perceived that thou art wondrously disposed unto wisdom. [He rubs his hands.] I also will profit therefrom.

APOLLONIUS. First I will tell thee of the long path I have trodden that I might possess the Doctrine—and shouldest thou discover in all my life but one evil deed, then shalt thou bid me stay. For he who hath offended in his deeds, his words shall be a stumbling-block.

DAMIS. [To S. Anthony.] A just man, is he not!

S. ANTHONY. Verily I think he speaketh truth.

APOLLONIUS. On the night of my birth my mother dreamed that she gathered flowers on the shores of a lake. The lightning flashed and she brought me forth to the sound of the voices of the swans who sang in her dream.

Until I was fifteen years of age, I was bathed daily three times in the fountain Asbadea, whose water giveth the dropsy to them that are forsworn; I was rubbed with leaves of the fleabane whereby I might be made pure. A princess of Palmyra came and sought me one even-

THE GOVERNOR OF CILICIA

ing, and offered unto me treasures that she knew were hidden in tombs. A slave of the temple of Diana slew herself for despair with the knife of the sacrifice; and the governor of Cilicia, when that he had come to an end of all his promises, cried out, before all my family, that he would put me to death. But he it was who died, three days later, slain by the Romans.

DAMIS. [To S. Anthony, nudging him with his elbow.] Said I not so! How wondrous a man!

APOLLONIUS. Throughout four years following did I keep complete silence after the manner of the Pythagoreans. The most sudden pain forced not a sigh from me; when I entered into the theatre men withdrew from me as though I were a spirit.

DAMIS. Wouldest thou have done this, thou?

APOLLONIUS. When the time of my silence was accomplished, I, I alone, took it upon me to instruct the priests who had lost the knowledge of their forefathers, and I gave forth this prayer: "O Gods!..."

S. ANTHONY. Wherefore "Gods"? The Gods? What saith he?

DAMIS. Let be, let him speak on, be silent.

APOLLONIUS. Then did I set forth to learn all worships and to question all oracles. I have held converse with the wise men of the Ganges, with the soothsayers of Chaldaea, with the wizards of Babylon. I have gone up into the fourteen mountains of Olympus, I have plumbed the lakes of Scythia, I have measured the breadth of the desert.

DAMIS. All this is truth. I, even I, was with him.

APOLLONIUS. At first I went from Pontus even to the sea of Hyrcania, I passed around it; and I went down unto Nineveh through the country of the Baraomates wherein is buried Bucephalus. At the gates of the town there was a statue of a woman clad after the fashion of the strange nations. A man drew nigh unto me.

DAMIS. It was I, good master, it was I ! At once I
loved thee. Thou wert sweeter than a maiden and
more beautiful than a god.

APOLLONIUS. [Not hearing him.] He desired to
come with me that he might interpret for me.

DAMIS. But thou didst answer and say that thou hadst
understanding of all tongues, and that thou couldest
divine all thoughts. Then did I kiss the hem of thy
mantle, and I set forth behind thee to walk in thy footsteps.

APOLLONIUS. After Ctesiphon we entered upon the
lands of Babylon.

DAMIS. The satrap cried aloud to see one so pale.

S. ANTHONY. The story is strange !

DAMIS. Surely it was on the morrow, master, that we
met that great tigress who had eight young in her womb ?
Then didst thou say : " Our sojourn in the house of
the king shall be for a year and eight months." Never
could I understand it. . . .

APOLLONIUS. The king received me standing up,
nigh unto a throne of silver, in a round hall the ceiling
whereof was covered with stars ; and from it hung by
threads that none could see, four great birds wrought
of gold, and their two wings were spread out.

S. ANTHONY. Can such things be upon earth ?

DAMIS. That is a great city, that Babylon ! All they
that dwell therein are rich ; the houses are painted
blue, and they have gates of bronze and staircases that
go down unto the river.

            [He draws on the ground with his staff.]
Behold, so is the fashion of it. Moreover, there are
temples and open places, baths and conduits of water.
The palaces are covered with red copper ; and within !
Ah ! couldest thou but know them !

APOLLONIUS. On the north wall there is a tower of
white marble that beareth a second, a third, a fourth,
a fifth tower, and there be yet three more towers !

These towers be sepulchres . . . the eighth is a chapel wherein is a bed. None may enter therein save the woman chosen by the priests for the God Bel. The King of Babylon gave it unto me for a dwelling-place.

DAMIS.   As for me, none heeded me.   I went about the streets alone and I learnt the customs of the people; I saw their workshops; I beheld the great engines that bear the water into the gardens. Yet it wearied me that I was sundered from my master.

APOLLONIUS.   At the end of a year and eight months . . .   [S. Anthony starts.]
. . . on an evening we went forth from Babylon by the way that leadeth to the land of India.   Under the light of the moon we beheld a Demon.

DAMIS.   Ay, in truth!   She leapt on her iron hoof. She neighed like unto an ass; she ran among the rocks. But he called curses upon her and she vanished.

S. ANTHONY.   What shall come of this, what shall follow?

APOLLONIUS.   [Continuing.]   At Taxilla, Phraortes, the King of the Ganges, showed unto us his bodyguard of black men, whose stature was five cubits in height; in the gardens of his palace under a tent of green brocade he showed unto us a great elephant whom his women delighted to sprinkle with sweet perfumes. Round his tusks he had necklaces of gold, and on one of these it was written : " The son of Jupiter hath vowed Ajax holy unto the sun."   For he was the elephant of Porus who had fled from Babylon after the death of Alexander.

DAMIS.   Ay!   They had found him again in a forest.

S. ANTHONY.   They speak overmuch, even as drunken men.

APOLLONIUS.   Phraortes made us to sit at his table. It was covered with great fruits laid upon wide leaves, and on it were horned antelopes.

2) p. 197

DAMIS.   It was a strange land !   The lords as they drank, delighted to cast darts beneath the feet of a child that danced.   But I like not that sport; evil might happen therefrom.

APOLLONIUS.   When I was ready to depart, the king gave unto me a parasol, and said unto me: " I have upon the shores of the Indus an herd of white camels. When thou hast no further need of them, breathe into their ears and they will return."

DELIGHTED TO CAST DARTS BENEATH THE FEET OF A CHILD.

We went down the banks of the river; we walked by night in the light of the fireflies that shone in the cane. The slave sang a song to drive away the serpents, and our camels bowed their loins as they passed beneath the trees as it were under low doorways.

Upon a day a black child who held in his hand a wand of gold led us to the college of the wise men.   Sarchas, their head man, spake unto me of my forefathers and of all my thoughts, of all my deeds and of all my lives. He had been the river Indus, and he recalled unto me that I had guided boats on the Nile in the days of the King Sesostris.

DAMIS. But as for me, they said nought unto me, so that I know not who I had been.

        [S. Anthony gazes at them with amazement.]

S. ANTHONY. Their aspect is dim as it were shadows.

APOLLONIUS. And we went on our way toward the ocean. On the shores thereof we came upon the Dog-headed Ape-folk, glutted with milk, returning from their journeying in the isle of Taprobane. With them was the Indian Venus, the black and white woman, who danced naked in the midst of the apes. Around her waist were hung timbrels of ivory and her laughter was beyond measure.

The warm waves drave white pearls before us upon the sand, the amber crackled beneath our footsteps, the bones of whales whitened in the clefts of the cliffs, and long nests of green weed hanging to their ribs swung in the wind.

Continually the earth shrank, at the last it was less than the breadth of a sandal. We stood still, we cast drops of sea-water towards the sun, we turned to our right hand that we might return.

We returned through the country of silver by way of the country of the Gangarides, by the headland Comaria, through the country of the Sachalites, and of the Adramites, and of the Homerites; then did we cross the Cassanian Mountains, we passed over the Red Sea and the island of Topazus, we entered into Ethiopia by way of the kingdom of the Pigmies.

S. ANTHONY. [Aside.] How great is the earth!

DAMIS. And when we had entered into our own place once more, all they that we had known aforetime were dead.   [S. Anthony bows his head.]

APOLLONIUS. [Resumes.] Then did men begin to speak of me in the world. The pestilence was laying

>) p. 197

waste Ephesus; I caused them to stone an aged beggar. . . .

DAMIS.   And the pestilence departed !

S. ANTHONY.   What !   He driveth away sickness.

APOLLONIUS.   At Cnidus I healed him that loved Venus.

DAMIS.   Ay, a madman who had even promised to wed her.   Love of women, what of it !   Let it pass !   But love for a statue, what folly !   The Master laid his hand on the young man's heart and thereupon was his love quenched within him.

S. ANTHONY.   What !   He delivereth from devils ?

APOLLONIUS.   At Tarentum they were bearing the body of a young maid to be burnt, for she was dead.

DAMIS.   The Master touched her lips and she rose up and called her mother.

S. ANTHONY.   What !   He raiseth the dead !

APOLLONIUS.   I foretold his dominion unto Vespasianus.

S. ANTHONY.   What !   He divineth the future !

APOLLONIUS.   Seated at table with him, at the baths at Baiae . . .

DAMIS.   There was at Corinth . . .

S. ANTHONY.   Forgive me, strangers, the hour is late.

DAMIS.   A young man called Menippus . . .

S. ANTHONY.   It is the hour of the first watch; get you gone !

APOLLONIUS.   A dog entered, bearing in his mouth a severed hand. . . .

DAMIS.   One night, in the outskirts of the city, he met a woman . . .

S. ANTHONY.   Hear ye me not ?   Depart from me !

APOLLONIUS.   He prowled hither and thither among the beds.

S. ANTHONY.   Enough, enough !

APOLLONIUS.   They would drive him away, but I . . .

DAMIS. Then Menippus went unto her house; they loved one another.

APOLLONIUS. And beating upon the pavement with his tail, he laid that hand on the knees of Flavius.

MENIPPUS WENT UNTO HER HOUSE.

DAMIS. But in the morning, during the lessons in the school, Menippus was pale . . .

S. ANTHONY. [Leaping up.] Yet again ! Nay, let them continue since there is not . . .

DAMIS. The Master said unto him : " O fair young man, thou dost cherish a serpent; a serpent doth

E

cherish thee! When shall be the espousals?" And we went unto the wedding, every one of us . . .

S. ANTHONY. I do wrong, of a surety I do wrong to hearken unto all this.

DAMIS. Even at the entrance to the hall serving-men busied themselves, doors opened; yet heard we neither the sound of footsteps, nor the sound of doors. The Master sat him down nigh unto Menippus. Thereupon was the bride wroth against the wise men. But the golden vessels that were upon the tables vanished, the cupbearers, the cooks, and they that bore the baskets of bread, disappeared; the roof flew away, the walls fell down, and Apollonius alone was left standing, and at his feet was the woman, weeping bitterly. For she was a demon who did glut goodly young men with love that she might devour their flesh—for nought is of greater worth for such kind of evil spirits than the blood of lovers.

APOLLONIUS. Wouldest thou know the skill . . .

S. ANTHONY. I would know nought! Get you gone!

DAMIS. What ill have we done unto thee?

S. ANTHONY. None . . . howbeit . . . nay, let them depart!

APOLLONIUS. On the night when we came unto the gates of Rome. . . .

S. ANTHONY. [Quickly.] Ay, ay! Speak to me of the city of the popes!

APOLLONIUS. [Continuing.] A drunken man approached us, singing in a sweet voice. He sang a wedding song of Nero, and he had power to slay any that should hearken heedlessly thereunto. He bore upon his back in a box of ivory a silver chord taken from the emperor's lute. I raised my shoulders. He cast mud into our faces; then did I undo my girdle and I laid it in his hands.

DAMIS. Thou wert greatly in error!

x) p. 198

APOLLONIUS. In the night the emperor summoned *see note to*
me unto his house; he was playing at knucklebones
with Sporus, and he leant the elbow of his left arm
upon an agate table. He turned him away, and bent his
pale eyebrows, and said unto me: "Wherefore dost
thou not fear me?" And I made answer unto him:
"Forasmuch as God who hath made thee terrible hath
made me without fear."

S. ANTHONY. [Dreamily.] There is therein somewhat not to be discovered that affrighted me. [Silence.]

DAMIS. [Beginning again in a shrill voice.] Nay, all
the folk of Asia can tell thee.

S. ANTHONY. [Leaping up.] Time lacketh! Tell it
another day! I am sick!

DAMIS. But hearken! At Ephesus he saw men slay
Domitianus who was at Rome . . .

S. ANTHONY. [Forcing a laugh.] Can this be!

DAMIS. Ay, in the theatre, in full daylight, on the
fourteenth day after the calends of October, he cried
out, on a sudden: "Cæsar is being slain!" and he said
further from time to time: "He rolleth about on the
ground; see how he doth struggle! He raiseth himself; he striveth to fly; the doors are shut! Lo! It is
finished! Behold him dead!" And verily, on that day,
Titus Flavius Domitianus was slain as thou knowest.

S. ANTHONY. [Reflecting.] Without the help of the
Evil One . . . verily . . .

APOLLONIUS. He, even that Domitianus, had wished
to put me to death! Damis had fled with Demetrius
at my command and I remained alone in my *illustration*
prison. . . . *next page*

DAMIS. It was wondrous hardihood, that is sure.

APOLLONIUS. Towards the fifth hour the soldiers led
me to the tribunal. Mine oration was fully prepared; I
held it beneath my cloak. . . .

DAMIS. We others were on the shores of Puteoli! We
deemed thee dead; we wept, each was returning to his

home, when, towards the sixth hour, on a sudden thou
didst appear.

S. ANTHONY. [Aside.] Even as Jesus!

DAMIS. We trembled, but thou saidst unto us:
"Touch me!" . . .

S. ANTHONY. Nay, that cannot be! Ye lie; surely ye
lie.

DAMIS. Then did we depart all together.

I REMAINED ALONE IN MY PRISON.

[Silence. Damis considers S. Anthony; Apollonius
    draws near to him and shouts in his ear.]

I have been down into the cave of Trophonius, the son
of Apollo! I pour offerings of wine through the ears of
the great jars! I know the prayers of the people of India!
I have kneaded for the women of Syracuse the members
of roseate honey that they bear shrieking over the mountains. I have taken the scarf of the Receivers of Contention! I have clasped the serpent of Sabasius against
my heart! I have laved Cybele in the waters of the

2) p. 198

Campanian gulfs, and I have passed three moons in the caverns of Samothracia.

DAMIS. [Laughing foolishly.] He! he! he! Amid the mysteries of the Kindly Goddess!

APOLLONIUS. Wilt thou come with us, and see greater stars and new gods?

S. ANTHONY. Nay! Go your way alone!

DAMIS. Let us depart!

S. ANTHONY. Begone! Flee!

APOLLONIUS. We go to the north, to the land of the swans and the snows. On the white desert doth gallop the horned roebuck whose eyes weep for the cold; the blind horse-footed folk crush the plant of the further seas with their hooves.

DAMIS. Come! It is dawn, the cock hath crowed, the horse hath neighed, the sail is set.

S. ANTHONY. Nay, the cock hath not crowed! I hear the cricket in the sand and I see the moon that stayeth ever in her place.

APOLLONIUS. Beyond the mountains, afar off, yonder, we shall pluck the apple of the Western Isles and in the perfume thereof we shall search out the cause of love. We shall smell the sweet odour of the myrrh of roses that bringeth death unto the weak. We shall bathe in the lake of roseate oil that is in the island Junonia. Thou shalt see, asleep upon the primroses, the great lizard who waketh once in every fivescore years what time the carbuncle of his eyes is ripened and falleth. The stars tremble like the gaze in men's eyes, the water-falls sing like harps, the flowers open and their breath is as the rapture of wine; thy spirit shall wax greater in the wind, and in thine heart, as in thy face. . . .

DAMIS. Master! It is time! The wind riseth, the swallows awaken, the leaf of the myrtle hath flown away!

APOLLONIUS. Yea, let us depart.

S. ANTHONY.   Nay, I remain !

APOLLONIUS.   Wouldest thou that I shew thee where groweth the plant Balis that raiseth the dead ?

DAMIS.   Ask him to give thee the tamer of men that draweth silver and iron and brass.

APOLLONIUS.   [Offering him a small round ring of copper.]   Wouldest thou the wayfarer's ward ? behold it !   Nay, take it !   Thou canst descend into the burning mountains, thou canst pass through the fire and fly in the air.

S. ANTHONY.   They hurt me, they hurt me sorely !

DAMIS.   Thou shalt understand the speech of all beings created, their roaring, their neighing, and their cooing.

APOLLONIUS.   Yea, for I have found out the secret of Tiresias, of that I am assured.

DAMIS.   Ay, and furthermore he knoweth songs that compel whomsoever thou mayest desire to come unto thee.

APOLLONIUS.   I have learned from the Arabians the speech of the vultures, and I have read in the grottoes of Strompharabarnax the fashion whereby to affright the rhinoceros and to give sleep unto the crocodile.

DAMIS.   When we journeyed aforetime, we heard, through the bindweed, the white unicorns that ran. They lay flat upon their bellies that he might mount upon their backs.

APOLLONIUS.   Thou too shalt ride upon them.   Thou shalt take hold of their ears.   We will go, we will go !

S. ANTHONY.   [Weeping.]   Woe, woe !

APOLLONIUS.   What aileth thee ?   Come !

S. ANTHONY.   [Sobbing.]   Woe, woe !

DAMIS.   Draw tight thy girdle, tie up thy sandals !

S. ANTHONY.   [Sobbing the more.]   Woe, woe, woe, woe !

APOLLONIUS.   The while we fare I will expound unto thee the meaning of statues—wherefore Zeus sitteth, but Apollo standeth on his feet—wherefore Aphrodite is black at Corinth, four square at Athens, and of the form of a cone at Paphos.

S. ANTHONY. Ah! God! Let them depart, let them depart from me!

APOLLONIUS. Knowest thou her, Aphrodite of the Heavens, who glittereth beneath her arch of stars? Have they told unto thee the mysteries of Aphrodite who foreseeth? Hast thou known the kiss of the Bearded Aphrodite, or thought upon the wrath of Astarte that rageth? Nay, fear not, I shall tear off their veils, I shall break their armour in pieces, thou shalt trample upon their temples, and we shall attain even unto Her that is Mysterious, Unchangeable, even to Her of the Masters, of the brave men, of the pure, Aphrodite that turneth away, She who driveth desire from its path and slayeth the flesh.

DAMIS. Ay, and whensoever we shall find the stone of a sepulchre, so it be large enough, we will play at the dice of Athene that is played in the night-time, in the fall of the year, under the full red moon.

APOLLONIUS. [Stamping his foot.] Why cometh he not?

DAMIS. [Also stamping his foot.] Up, away!

APOLLONIUS. [Gazing fixedly at S. Anthony.] Doubtest thou me?

DAMIS. [Threatening.] Thou dost doubt him? Call, Master, call unto the lion of Numidia, he that held within him the soul of Amasis.

S. ANTHONY. My God! My God! Shall they take me by force!

APOLLONIUS. What is thy desire? Needs but the time wherein to think upon it? . . .

S. ANTHONY. [Joining his hands.] I slip! Stay me!

APOLLONIUS. Is it Wisdom? Is it glory? Wouldest thou refresh thine eyes upon wet flower of jessamine? Wouldest thou feel thy body sink into the soft flesh of languishing women as it were into a billow of the sea?

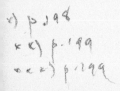

S. ANTHONY. [Holding his head and crying aloud in pain.] Again ! Again !

DAMIS. Ay, indeed ! The diamonds shall flow from the mountain rent open. The roses shall flower upon this thy cross. The sirens whose hinder parts are of the shell of the pearl shall cherish thee with their hair ; they shall soothe thee to sleep with their songs.

S. ANTHONY. O Holy Spirit, deliver me !

APOLLONIUS. Wouldest thou that I change me to a tree, to a leopard, to a river ?

S. ANTHONY. O Holy Virgin, Mother of God, pray for me !

APOLLONIUS. Wouldest thou that I compel the moon to go backward ?

S. ANTHONY. O Holy Trinity, save me !

APOLLONIUS. Wouldest thou that I show thee Jerusalem all alight for the Sabbath ?

S. ANTHONY. Jesus, Jesus, help me !

APOLLONIUS. Wouldest thou that I cause Jesus to appear ?

S. ANTHONY. [Bewildered.] What sayest thou ?

APOLLONIUS. Here, in this place ! . . . He and no other ! Thou shalt see the holes in His hands and the blood of His wound. He shall cast down His crown, He shall call His Father accursed, He shall bow down before me, His back shall be bowed.

DAMIS. [In a low voice, to S. Anthony.] Say that thou wouldest, say that thou wouldest !

S. ANTHONY. [Passes his hand over his face, casts scared eyes on every side, then rests his gaze on Apollonius.] Depart, get thee hence, thou accursed one ! Get thee back to hell !

APOLLONIUS. [Exasperated.] From hell do I come ! I am come forth from thence that I might lead thee thither ! The vats of nitre seethe, the coals flame, the steel teeth clap together, and the shadows gather close to the vent-holes to see thee pass.

S. ANTHONY. [Tearing his hair.] Me! Great God! Hell for me!

PRIDE. [Rising behind S. Anthony and laying her hand on his shoulder.] For such an holy man! Impossible!

DAMIS. [With enticing gestures.] Nay, good hermit, beloved Anthony, thou pure man, thou man of renown, thou whom none can praise to his due! Have no fear, it is but his fashion of speech, it is the manner of speech that he hath learnt of the men of the East; but he is good, he is holy, he can . . .

[Damis pauses, and S. Anthony looks at Apollonius, who begins to speak in a voice that is at once vehement and suave.]

APOLLONIUS. Yet, further away than all the worlds, beyond the heavens, above all shapes, shineth the world of thought, not to be attained, not to be entered, wholly filled of the Word. We shall set forth therefrom, we shall overpass in one leap the whole firmament, and thou shalt grasp in its infinity the Everlasting, the Being! Up, away! Give me thy hand!

[And suddenly the earth opens funnelwise and forms a great gulf. Apollonius grows and grows; blood-red clouds roll beneath his bare feet and his white tunic gleams like snow.

A circle of gold round his head quivers in the air with elastic motion. He holds out his left hand to S. Anthony and with his right hand he points to the sky; his mien is royal, inspired.]

S. ANTHONY. [Bewildered.] A tumult of desire uplifteth me unto heights that terrify me, the ground fleeth away like a wave, mine head is burst in sunder.

[He clings to the cross with all his strength.]

THE VALERIANS. Lo! Here be our knives!

THE CIRCONCELLIONS. [Reappearing.] Lo! Here be our daggers!

THE CARPOCRATIANS. Lo! Here be our flowers!

THE MONTANISTS.   Lo !   Here be our shirts of hair, our poisons, our crosses, our racks.

MAXIMILLA AND PRISCILLA.   [Weeping.]   O sweet Anthony !   Dost thou hear us ?   Come.

THE SABAEANS.   Come, pray with us in our temples of stone whose shape is the shape of stars.

THE MANICHAEANS.   Nay, fly unto the feast of the Sacred Chair.   Thou shalt sit in the seat of Manes.   We will rub thee with benzoin, thou shalt drink boiled wine, and thou shalt understand the twain Ordinances, the twelve Vessels, the five Natures, and the eight Worlds, with the Shoulderer who beareth the Earth upon his shoulders and He that holdeth in Glory, who hath six faces; he holdeth it between his fingers that it may not waver.

THE GNOSTICS.   We will open unto thee Knowledge and thou shalt ascend unto the shining Yokes who shall bear thee to the breast of the Eternal Abysm in the circle unchangeable of Fulfilment.

[Other Heresies arrive.]

S. ANTHONY.   [Tearing his hair.]   Ha !   they return !

SIMON MAGUS.   [With Understanding all clad in gold.]   Ay, and she returneth also !   She hath suffered even as thou hast, but now is she joyful, now is she prepared to sing without ceasing !   Dost thou deem her fair ?   Dost thou desire her ?   She is the Thought !   Love thou her !   Penitence doth brighten her life unto her, love consumeth her with fire.

S. ANTHONY.   How shall I pray ?   On whom shall I call ?

[THE FALSE PROPHETESS OF CAPPADOCIA passes at a gallop at the back of the scene, bending over the back of her tigress and shaking her torch.]

On me, on me !

THE DEADLY SINS.   [All cry out.]   On us, on us !

LUST.   Let thy flesh rejoice !

IDLENESS.   Think no more thereon !

AVARICE.   Seek for money !

ENVY.   God hateth thee !   Hate thou God !

THE CIRCONCELLIONS.   Slay thyself, slay thyself !
[The Heresies and the Sins surround S. Anthony.
Maximilla and Priscilla weep ;   Understanding begins
to sing ; Apollonius, with his white staff, traces
circles of fire in the air ; the Gnostics open their
books ; the False Prophetess, on the horizon, sways
upon her beast.]

S.   ANTHONY.   [Bewildered.]   O   Lord,   Lord !
Strengthen Thou my faith !   Give unto me hope !   Make
me to love Thee !   Increase Thy wrath twofold if it so
please Thee, but have pity, have pity !
[Three white figures, the Cardinal Virtues, appear
on the threshold of the chapel.   S. Anthony struggles
to free himself.]

I come to you !   Help ye me !

THE SINS.   What !   Thou wouldst drive us back !   We
are Rapture !

THE HERESIES.   What !   Thou dost forsake us !   Us,
the daughters of the Church, the manifold nature of the
Doctrine of Christ !   When we die, then shall she die
also !
[S. Anthony strives to win to the three Virtues.
Pride comes up behind him and pushes him in the
back and urges him forward.   Then the Heresies
draw away from him and the Sins retire.   Lust,
sighing, seats herself upon the pig and spreads out
thereon her fine spangled gown ;   Sloth falls asleep ;
Anger gnaws her nails ; Avarice stoops down and
grubs in the earth ; Envy holds her hand before her
eyes and gazes into the distance ; Greed crouches
down.   Pride remains standing up.]

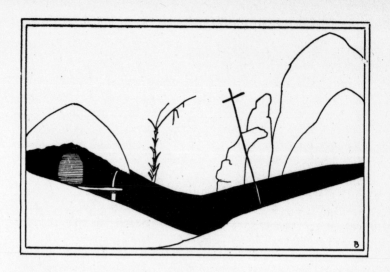

PART II

S. ANTHONY is in the chapel, between the three Cardinal Virtues. A great laugh is heard and the Devil appears, terrible, hideous, hairy—his mouth is set with tusks as of a boar; violet flames come out of his eyes. Pride straightens her stature again, Envy hisses, Lust scratches her loins, Avarice holds out her hand, Anger howls, Greed clacks her jaws together, Sloth sighs.

THE DEVIL. Aha! I will shut you up in Hell, I will scourge you with the lusts of another world that I may renew life unto your quenched strength! Is there no more? . . .

THE SINS. [All together.] It is Pride who hath saved him! We had even now caught him!

LUST. She freezeth the hearts of men in vows of godliness!

AVARICE. She casteth my treasures to the wind.

ANGER. She hath discovered mercy!

GREED. She hath ordained fasting!

IDLENESS. Her foot striketh me . . .

ENVY. She driveth me back! I rest never for running in her shadow!

PRIDE. [Descends one step of the chapel, turns her head on her shoulder, half closes her eyelids and replies.] Have I ever beseeched thee to follow me, O Envy? Why comest thou to suck from my breast the poison that swelleth it out? That it is that reneweth thy life, avow it! Thou, Avarice, thou dost delight to rest the gaze of thine eyes upon the gold of my palaces—it is I, O Anger, who give voice to thy drums! Knowest thou not, thou fool, Greed, the visions that I give unto thee? I carve thy dishes, I feast thy followers! Mine the challenges of victual, mine the wagers of drink whereof men burst, and mine the cruelty of the guttler after his meal!

THE SINS. Hearken to her boasting! Hear how she babbleth!

PRIDE. But thou, Lust, thou shouldest cherish me! I fill the hearts of the highborn women, and thence cometh to their breasts such calm and fair movement of majesty. Mine is the rustling silk, the ringing bracelet, the creaking shoe, the shameless raiment, the wide-opened eye, and the bitter excitement that ariseth for unseemly posture. I am Daring, I urge thee unto great venturings! All despised things do dry them before my hearth . . . dost thou hear the proud neighing of whoredoms triumphant?

THE SINS. What matter! We it is who do suffer!

ENVY. Nay, Father, on me shouldest thou have pity. My nails are worn away; do thou sharpen them!

GREED. Lo, I am full even to the throat! The skin of my belly rendeth in sunder. But ever I hunger, ever am I athirst! Devise thou somewhat that shall be without all victual, nay, without the creation itself!

AVARICE. Yet have I ravaged the earth and pierced mountains, I have slaughtered beasts and hewn down forests and sold all that might be sold—the body and the soul, tears and laughter, kisses and thoughts! O could I but catch the rays of the sun and melt them into pieces of gold!

ANGER.   Anoint me, O My Father, with vinegar distilled by Hatred.   For I fall for faintness at the smile of Lust and the enticing of Avarice.   Let me break, let me grind unto powder, let me slay! Meseemeth I have the Ocean within my breast.   Wrath crasheth against wrath and I quiver as do the cliffs to the beating of the tides.

SLOTH.   [Yawning.] On a soft quilt of down . . . to the breath of a soft wind . . . in a bark . . . doing nought . . . ah . . . ah!   [She falls asleep.]

LUST.   I would feel that I sink without ceasing into rapture, as it were into a gulf that endeth not . . . where is it, that which I seem to pursue through possession? For I see, darkly, in the heart of pleasure, as it were a dim sun the rays whereof dazzle me and the heat of it enkindleth me.

O that I had hands over all my body wherewith to fondle! O that I had lips wherewith to kiss, at the tips of my fingers!

THE DEVIL.   Cry not so loud! Labour all ye together. Help me!   [He points to S. Anthony.]
Bring to flower in his thought new imaginations, and then shall he know dreadful despair and rendings of covetousness and fury of weariness! Make him to pass from the languor of Sloth even into the frenzy of Anger! Let him be smitten suddenly with great hunger before the lighted tables of great feasts; let him trail, rutting, over the floor of his hut, let him compare him unto them that be happy, and let him abhor the world! Let him be exalted in repentance, let him burst in sunder for pride! Make ye him yours! Make ye him mine! Go! Call together the spirits of evil, your sons and your sons' sons, with all fevers, all visions of madness, all bitterness unbounded!

ANGER

[The Devil withdraws to the back of the scene and sits him down upon the body of Sloth; he places Lust between his legs, and then unfolds, like a bat, his great greenish wings whereunder the other Sins come and shelter them.

Pride, from behind him, passes her head over his shoulder and kisses him on the forehead.]

S. ANTHONY. [Between the Virtues.] Shall they return?

HOPE. We are here! Fear nought!

FAITH. [Standing upright, straight and motionless.] Believe that which thou seest not, believe that thou knowest not—and ask not to see that thou · hopest, neither to know that thou dost worship! The unbelievers hear but the voice of the flesh and the testimony of the understanding, but the sons of Christ despise the flesh and betake them to the speech of the Word. For the Word is eternal, but the flesh shall die and the understanding shall vanish away as it were the perfume of wine that is poured out upon the ground! Hope for grace that thou mayest obtain it, keep it that it may increase, despair not that it may return unto thee!

CHARITY. [On her knees, as though she were beside a dying man.] Fast for sinners, pray for them that worship idols, scourge thyself for the unclean! Pluck out of thy soul all love of this world! For as these be lessened so shall thy soul stand higher and higher, even as the pine-trees upon the mountains, whose leaves are diminished even as they draw nearer unto the heavens!

S. ANTHONY. Speak on, speak on! Infinite peace entereth within me!

HOPE. [Lifting her great blue eyes unto heaven.] The bark was tossed upon the waters and Jesus slept. They heard in the darkness the wind crying in great wrath. "Arise, Master," they said, "drive away the winds!" The bark is thine heart which beareth Faith. Suffer

her not to sleep, for the tempest was strengthened
because the Lord slept. When He opened again his
eyelids, it passed away.

If then thou wouldest cross from the one shore unto
the other, have no heed for the lightning that dazzleth

NEARER!   NEARER!

thee nor for the waves that deafen thine ears—take no
thought for the oars, nor for the sail, nor for the night,
nor for the storm! Is not the Lord with thee?

S. ANTHONY. [Clinging close to the Virtues.]
Nearer! Nearer!

FAITH. Hosanna! Glory to God!
                    [The Sins all at once begin to howl.]
S. ANTHONY. [Leaping up.] Save me, save me!
THE VIRTUES. Be of good Courage! O Anthony!
The temptations of the Evil One shall assail always the
faith of mankind in the Lord, and the sanctuaries shall
be shaken together in harmony by the blasts of the
tempest that shall beat upon their walls.
THE SINS. Yet at the last shall they fall to pieces, for
we are eternally young even as the dawn, we are strong
as the flesh, we are undying even as the Spirit.

(*VARIANT : Here is intercalated a passage
        suppressed by Flaubert, but which figures
        in the manuscript of 1856 on a page
        gummed on to p. 76.*)

FAITH. I shall increase my stature. I shall become
valorous, a conqueror.
ANGER. I shall curse. I shall persecute. I shall burn.
I shall slay.
CHARITY. I shall pour forth my blood in preaching.
I shall give alms freely and consolation. I shall wash
away all sorrow, from the sore of the leper even to the
mocking of the unbelievers.
PRIDE. I shall fill the churches with the pomp of
Assyria. I shall place therein vessels of gold and purple,
and inlaid work of diamonds, and canopies of ostrich
feathers—and the heritor of S. Peter shall put forth the
satin of his sandals for kings to kiss.
AVARICE. I shall sell the bones of martyrs, redemp-
tion of sins, the flesh of God, and the joys of heaven.
HOPE. The sound of the church bells shall be spread
abroad in the winds as it were the voices of the seraphim
that sing; and all the people shall bless the Most High
in the sounding speech of the priests.
LOGIC. The fury of the Devil shall drive them to

F

madness without end; their speech shall overflow, there shall be rivers of blood.

FAITH. The sweet odour of mine incense shall purify souls, and they that be strong shall free them from all love that they may the better brighten the life unto the love celestial that shall burn them without ceasing.

LUST. Ay, and man, ever agape after my joys, shall place in his sanctuaries his Goddess that dieth not, Woman! He shall dream of her crowned with stars, smiling, fair-haired, with ruddy cheeks, her breasts swollen with milk even as Cybele of the Syrians!

LOGIC. Thus shall every man in this worship satisfy the several lusts of his own heart. The master shall love it for the submission that it doth compel, and the slave for the freedom that it promiseth, the poet for the manner of its ordering, the wise man for its godly teaching; yet others shall love it for its statecraft or for its great age; for we shall breathe into it with our breath and enkindle it with our heat seeing that we are young eternally.

(End of Variant.)

THE DEVIL. Yea! Let us enter! Let us drive them forth!

A CHILD'S VOICE. Mother, mother, await me!
    [Science runs up; a child, white-haired, and frail of feet.]

SCIENCE. [To Pride.] Ah, didst thou know how sick am I, what confusion there is within mine head! O my mother, to what end be these many writings that I spell out? Now and then the wind quencheth my torch, and then am I alone, weeping in the darkness.

THE SINS. What aileth him? What is his need?

AVARICE. Wilt thou come with me?

SCIENCE. Nay, I have polished thy diamonds, I have beaten out thy money, I have woven thy fine cloth.

*) p. 200

GREED. Wilt thou come with me?

SCIENCE. Nay, I know how to make the vine grow and after what manner men hunt beasts.

ENVY. Wilt thou come with me?

SCIENCE. Nay, I have no hate.

ANGER. Wilt thou come with me?

SCIENCE. Nay, nought can irk me to wrath.

SLOTH. Rest thee!

SCIENCE. Nay . . . even as the stars on which she doth gaze my thought goeth forth ever of herself, she accomplisheth her journey that none may withstand, and together we pass in great courses about the heavens.

LUST. Wilt thou come with me?

SCIENCE. Nay! I have persecuted thee with curious zeal, I have seen the paint upon thy face sweat for thy strivings wherewith thou didst strive to get thee pleasure. Thou, O Lust, thou goest about in freedom, thou art beautiful, thou liftest up thine head. At all cross-roads of the soul is thy song heard; and thou dost pass at the end of a thought, even as an harlot passeth at the end of a street. But thou sayest nought of the sores that eat away their heart, nor of the weariness without measure that drippeth from love as from a sore. Get thee hence, begone! I am weary of thy face.

Rather do I love the weed on the flank of the cliffs, than thine hair unknotted! Rather do I love the light of the moon lengthening in the tides, than thy distraught gaze that drowneth itself in fondness. Rather do I love marble, or colours, or insects or pebbles! Rather would I have my loneliness than thine house, and my despair than thy sorrows.

PRIDE. Comfort thee, my child! Thou shalt grow greater in stature! I will give thee to drink of good bitter wine, thou shalt make thy bed upon herbs of the field.

[S. Anthony is still on his knees between the three Cardinal Virtues; they spread out their white robes in front of him to shelter him, but]

THE DEVIL. [Takes Science by the hand and points to Faith inside the chapel.] Behold her! Thou shalt utterly make an end of her!

SCIENCE. [Kicking against the door.] Open unto me! The hour hath come!

THE SINS. [Scratching the wall with their nails.] Ha! The sky is shaken! All things shall fall to pieces!

SCIENCE. I shall tell unto thee the beginnings of things! I shall display the certitude thereof before thee! Thou shalt see. . . .

FAITH. No matter! Say on!

S. ANTHONY. Our Father, which art in heaven. . . .
        [The Sins howl, he turns away from them.]
Ah me! What should I do?

FAITH. Pray to the Son!

SCIENCE. Yet hath Origen forbidden that!

FAITH. Make supplication unto the angels!

PRIDE. But they can have no part, as thou hast, in the virtue of Jesus Christ, seeing that they are without the body! They have not suffered, merit is not in them; they would envy thee did they know of thee.

CHARITY. Think upon the martyrs!

SCIENCE. But all worship, all love, all wickedness of whatsoever kind, these have had their martyrs, even as thy God.

S. ANTHONY. Ah me! I would fain go and pray upon their tombs!

GREED. Ay, forsooth, by night, when the little lamps shrivel in the fog in the midst of the dishes of meat and the cups that smoke . . . the faithful hold feast for the salvation of the dead, and they return thence in the morning, they stagger to and fro in the long grass.

S. ANTHONY. [Pulling the Virtues by their robes.] Answer! Speak unto them! Be swift in doing!

FAITH. Doctrine. . . .

LOGIC. [Interrupting her.] There is nought doth stablish it!

CHARITY. The loving-kindness of the Lord. . . .
[Envy bursts out laughing.]
HOPE. The joys of Heaven. . . .
LOGIC. Nay, which Heaven? Is it the garden of
Moses, or Jerusalem the city of light, or the unclean
heaven of Epiphanes? Shalt thou go into the stars of
Manes, into the Blessed Fields of the idolators, or into
the dim heaven of fire of the wise men?

THEY STAGGER TO AND FRO IN THE LONG GRASS.

Shalt thou take with thee into the mysterious firmament
thy mortal body, raised up again? Yet, saith Paul of
Tarsus, flesh and blood do not enter therein!
  [S. Anthony can no longer hear the voices of the
  Virtues whose lips continue to quiver in rapid and
  monotonous movement, like the leaves of a tree
  shaken. He listens intently and stands gaping.]
LOGIC. Wherefore tempted He Judas when He gave
the bag into his trust!
ENVY. Himself He yielded not, for an angel bore Him
up in His Agony.

LOGIC. He was no whit clean of sin forasmuch as He was born of a woman.

SCIENCE. He was of the seed of Rahab the harlot, and Bathsheba the adulteress, and Tamar who sinned with her brother.

LOGIC. Wherefore came He not into the house of Lazarus? Wherefore rejected He His mother? Wherefore had he need of baptism? Wherefore feared He to die?

S. ANTHONY. [To the Virtues.] Ah me! Ye grow pale!

ALL TOGETHER. Aha! Thou shalt sing! Thou shalt dance! Thou shalt laugh!

        [He runs, bewildered, seeking to flee.]

PRIDE. Enough hast thou prayed, Anthony! Thou hast grace!

S. ANTHONY. What? . . . Yet are the Temptations still there?

        [The Devil makes a swift sign to the Sins.]

PRIDE. They are there no more! Behold!

        [The Sins have disappeared.]

S. ANTHONY. [Looking round.] Yea, it is true.

    [Pride strikes Faith in the face with the serpent she holds in her bosom, and the Virtues disappear without the hermit perceiving it.]

PRIDE. [Resumes.] Come forth from thy chapel! Come forth! Breathe the air!

S. ANTHONY. [He is now outside.] How soft is the night! How pure is the air! How the stars glitter!

    [He walks up and down, his arms swinging loose. Pride stalks behind him, in his shadow.]

How can other men see to their salvation that have wives and trades and all the troubles of this life? As for me, thanks be to Heaven, nought troubleth me. In the morning I make my prayer—that is the beginning; then I give food unto my pig—that maketh me merry;

then do I sweep mine hut clean, I take up my baskets; at last cometh the hour of prayer. . . .

[The Devil laughs in the background.]

A while since I was much tormented, yea, I was evilly tormented. . . . Nay, I will not let those wicked thoughts return! I know now the manner of their onset.

[His foot strikes against something; he picks it up.]

Ha! A silver goblet! and therein is a piece of gold. . . . What? . . . another, and yet another! Ah! Wonder!

[The goblet fills with gold pieces.]

Lo! The colour of it! It changeth! . . . It is emerald! Lo! It becometh wholly clear and full of light . . . it is a diamond! It burneth me! Ah!

[Rubies, turquoises, onyxes, pearls and topazes pour over the edge of the goblet. S. Anthony looses his hands from it; it stays in the air, the stem lengthens, and the cup of it opens out above like a great lotus flower, whence streams continually a cascade of precious stones.]

Nay! I will not!

[He kicks the goblet; the vision disappears.]

When shall I be at rest? What a great sinner am I! I can have no thought but I lose my soul! Hither, hither, pangs of the flesh!   [He leaps to his scourge.]

THE PIG. [Waking up.] What a dream!

I was on the shores of a lake. I entered therein, for I was athirst, and the wave thereof changed suddenly into water wherein dishes had been washed. Then a warm wind, as it were a vapour of the cooking pots, drave toward my mouth broken bits of victual that floated afar off, hither and thither. The more I ate thereof, the more I craved to eat, and I went forward continually, making with my body a furrow in the clear broth. I swam therein, distraught, I said unto myself: "Hasten!" The rottenness of all the world was spread out round about me to satisfy the desire of my belly. In the darkness I saw dimly clots of black blood, plashes

of oil, blue entrails, the droppings of all beasts, with the
vomits of feasts and the green drip that sweateth from
sores. It thickened beneath me; my four paws sank
therein; a rain of retching that fell fine as needles,
pricked mine eyes, but ever I swallowed, for it was
good. The lake boiled ever more and more, it pressed
upon my ribs, it was unbounded, it burned me, it choked
me; I would flee, but I could not move; I closed my
mouth, but needs must I open it again; then did other
things of themselves fling themselves therein, all bubbled
in my belly, all lapped against mine ears. I howled,
my throat rattled, I ate . . . pah, pah! I would fain
break mine head against the stones that I may rid me
of my thought!

S. ANTHONY. [Scourging himself.] Ah! No
matter! Be not a coward! Ah! There, sinner, there!
Suffer! Weep! Cry aloud! Yet again cry aloud!
What? I shall count even to five score, even to a
thousand!

[He pauses.]
Nay, thou shalt not triumph over me, thou weakness of
the flesh! . . . Bleed, bleed!

[He recommences.]
Stay! . . . I feel nought now! . . . Doubtless the
pricks catch in my vesture.

[He undoes his robe, which falls as far as his girdle.
He resumes his scourging, the blows ring.]
Aha! On the breast! On the back! On the arms! On
the loins! On the face! I crave for scourging, it calmeth
me. Stronger! . . . Woe! Woe! . . . yet do I now
desire to laugh. Ha, ha, ha! It is as though hands
fondled me over all my body . . . tear we it! Ah me!
My sinews break! What then? [He stops.]
It may be the ravishment doth lessen the pangs of the
flesh; I will crush it out therefrom; I will have no
mercy upon it, nay, nay!

[He lashes himself in frenzy. The Devil, standing

behind him, has taken his arm and is urging it in
furious movement.]
In despite of myself mine arm continueth! Who urgeth
me? What torment! What rapture! I can no more,
my being melteth . . . I die.

[He swoons away and he thinks he sees: a street
with flowering plane-trees; to the left hand, in the
angle, a little house whose half-open door gives
sight of a court bordered by Doric columns that
support the dwelling-rooms of the first storey;
between the columns can be distinguished other
doors covered with blue lacquer and adorned with
inlay of copper.

In the middle of the courtyard, on her knees, a
woman, clad in a yellow tunic, is filling baskets and
boxes. Standing upright near her, her back against
a column and watching her at her task, is another
woman, all in white; her garment is fastened on her
shoulders with a golden brooch, and it hangs thence
in great straight folds, and the toes of her bare feet,
shod in openworked sandals, peer out beyond it.
Two wide fair tresses, plaited in symmetrical
diamond plaits, spread out over her ears; they
meet and are attached behind to a garland of fine
pearls, whence falls in tiny curls all the rest of her
hair.

THE COURTESAN. Hasten, Lampito! I must depart
ere even the mariners be awake!

[The kneeling woman sobs; the other continues:]
Hast thou put the ointment of Delos into the leaden
boxes, and my sandals of Patara into the satchel scented
with the powder of iris?

LAMPITO. Yea, Mistress! and here is the loosestrife
for thine hair, here be the flies' feet for thine eyebrows
and the roots of bear's breech for thy face.

THE COURTESAN. Hide in the bottom thereof,
beneath my robes from Sybaris, the pine-wood tablets

that constrain my waist, forget not the stone of the wild ass that the wizard sold unto me, nor the firestone of Egypt that preventeth childbirth.

LAMPITO. Ah! Mistress, shall I then see thee no more?

> [She weeps. S. Anthony sees himself—sees another S. Anthony—in the street, before the Courtesan's house.]

THE COURTESAN. Furthermore put in all that I have of spikenard, of oil of roses, of saffron—and especially of almond oil; for they tell me that it is bad in that country. Forasmuch as he loveth me since that day when he was aware at his awakening that his beard smelled sweet for that he had slept with his head upon my breast, surely I must see to it that my body give forth soft odours.

LAMPITO.   He hath great riches, Mistress, this king of Pergamos?

THE COURTESAN.   Ay, Lampito, he is rich! and I would not beg of my lovers of aforetime when I am old, nor be consenting unto mariners. In five years, in ten years, I shall have much gold, O Lampito! I shall return,—and even if I cannot build a portico at Sicyone as did Lamia, nor, as did Cleine the flute player, people the Peloponnesus with the brazen statues of me, yet—this at least is my hope—I shall have the wherewithal to feed my little Syracusan hound with the cakes of Carthage. I shall get me an household after the manner of the Persians. I shall have peacocks in my courtyard and robes of purple from Hermione broidered with sprays of golden ivy—and they shall say: "Lo! It is Demonassa the Corinthian who returneth to dwell among us! Happy is he whom she doth love!" For it is ever the rich woman, O Lampito, who is desired!

LAMPITO. Mistress, the young men of Athens will die of weariness.

> [S. Anthony advances towards the door.]

THE COURTESAN. Who is it walketh in the street, Lampito?

LAMPITO. Doubtless it is the wind blowing in the plane-trees, my mistress.

THE WIND OF THY SCARF.

THE COURTESAN. I fear the Archons; did they know that I would depart, they would stay me.

LAMPITO. But three mules await thee at the Golden Cross-roads, and with them a sure guide who knoweth the mountain passes.

THE FALSE S. ANTHONY. [In the street.] Shall I enter? Shall I refrain?

LAMPITO. Ah, me ! The feasts will be sad ! None could raise the striped skirt as thou couldest, in equal measure, in the Dorian bibasis, none could dance the martypsa in more wondrous wise ! When thou turnedst around about the couches, thy body flung back, thy right arm stretched out, clapping the black castanets in thy hands, the wind of thy scarf stirred the hair upon the foreheads of the guests who bowed them forward between the torches that they might see thy dance as it passed.   [The False S. Anthony stops.]

THE COURTESAN. Who is it sigheth without, Lampito ?

LAMPITO. Nay, it is no one, my mistress ! Doubtless it is the turtles that coo upon the terrace.

THE FALSE S. ANTHONY. Should I enter ?

LAMPITO. Thou didst drink the wine of Mendes in goblets from Carchedon. Thou didst seat thee upon the knees of the great men, and each one of them, holding thy waist, desired thee to say some word. The wise men were heated, they discoursed of Beauty; the painters waved their arms, they marvelled at the fashion of thy face; the poets grew pale, they shivered under their vesture.

Surely folk of a strange land shall not praise thee, when thou dost stretch thy body forward, even as a swimmer, over the harp of Egypt with the forty golden chords, nor when the hollow lute murmureth under the ivory bow, and thy mouth whose speech is soft is opened for the songs of the Sweet Singers. O thou Demonassa, whose eyebrows are curved even as the bow of Apollo, and whose face is beautiful as the quiet sea, no longer shalt thou know the long choirs of the feast of the Law-giver pass upon the road to Eleusis, nor the theatre of Bacchus, shrill with the voices of the players, nor the harbour where the folk walk in the evening.

THE COURTESAN. Lampito, one knocketh upon the door !

LAMPITO. Nay, Mistress, it is the screen beateth
against the wall.

THE FALSE S. ANTHONY. [Holding the knocker.]
My knees tremble, I shall not dare.

THE COURTESAN. [Walking up and down under the
colonnades, her head bowed, her arms hanging loose.]
Alas, alas! I must depart! . . . Farewell to the long
discourse in their halls with the beloved makers of
statues, farewell to the sound of the iron chisels that
rang on the marble of Paros. The Master, bare-armed,
kneaded the brown clay. From the stool whereon I
stood before him, I could see his great bow knit with
disquiet. On my body he sought for the shape that he
had imagined, and he was sore amazed, forasmuch as he
found it on a sudden to be yet more wondrous than the
shape within his thought; as for me, I laughed to see
the despair of his craft for the form of my knee-pan
and the dimples in my back.

[The False S. Anthony pushes open the door.]

LAMPITO. [Throwing herself upon Demonassa.]
Mistress, Mistress! It is that stranger who had bade me
say nought thereof . . . [All disappear.]

S. ANTHONY. [Rises up again.] Where was I? . . .
In a street in Athens? . . . yet have I never been there!
. . . No matter! I am persuaded that all things yonder
must be so ordered.

Whence cometh it that I still think thereon? . . . this
is evil! Yet wherefore? . . . the least of my desires is
so fenced about with stumbling-blocks that I can pass
to and fro therein at mine ease without any fear of peril.
Even had I let my desires have their will of me or ever
I came into the wilderness, now would the dream of
them not torment me . . . perchance. I should know
the kisses that slay the soul . . . the joy of accursed
love . . . the fierceness of pleasure . . .

[He strikes his forehead.]

Again! Again! Whither runneth my thought? At the

illustration on p. 78

last I do no more possess myself, so dispersed and wide-spread is mine own self.

[He folds his arms and sighs.]
Yet aforetime I was calm, I dwelt in the simplicity of my belief, and every morn when I awoke it was as though my soul flowered forth beneath the eye of God, as it were a meadow spread with dew steaming to the sun. Yea! Aforetime, in the beginning. . . . I had but departed from mine house.

THE PIG.   I have remembrance of a farmyard, between four walls, with a pool of mire, a great and rich dung-heap and a trough of new wood ever full of bran. I

THE FIERCENESS OF PLEASURE.

slept in the shadow, my snout resting upon red udders and I had ever in my throat the taste of the milk.

S. ANTHONY.   Who dwelleth now there in my father's house? Ah me! How bitterly wept my mother when I departed! Hath she ever thought of me? She must be very aged . . . very aged.

[He half closes his eyes and looks towards the horizon and sees afar off in the midst of the sands some little huts of grey mud under a grove of palm-trees whose boughs sway. Dogs trail themselves over the deserted sills, a herd of buffaloes passes; he can even make out, in the palisades of dry reeds, hens pecking wheat under the bellies of the asses.

But an aged woman who is spinning with a distaff comes out of her house and looks about her anxiously. She is bent double, wrinkled, lean, covered with rags; from time to time, to wipe her red eyelids, she takes her long hair in both hands— her hair that hangs over her shoulders, whiter and more tangled than the flax of her distaff; she murmurs :]

THE AGED WOMAN. The Publicans have taken away mine all! I am sick. . . . I am about to die . . . where is he?

S. ANTHONY. Here am I, my mother! It is I, it is I! I return unto thee!

[He runs forward with outstretched arms, but strikes against the rock and covers his face with blood from the impact. He looks round him. The lamp is burning, the pig is dozing, the fragments of baskets, lying on the ground, are lifted by the wind. He weeps.]

Ah me! I am wounded! . . . I suffer! . . . yet have I never harmed any man! Whence cometh all this? wherefore is it?   [Silence. He resumes :]
It were well that I fasten my thoughts upon somewhat that cannot change, and that I suffer not my thoughts to stray; but whereon shall I fasten them? . . . I will even assay to read that ancient book of the Scriptures that Paul the Solitary gave unto me when he was dying!

[He goes into his hut and brings forth a book, then sits down on a bench, turns the leaves over at random, then reads :]

"And Judah was comforted, and went up unto his sheepshearers." Verily that healeth me . . . mine understanding is clear again!   *)
"He and his friend, Hirah the Adullamite, the shepherd of his flocks." . . .

[A bleating is heard on the horizon.]

x) p. xov (see p. 80)

It is as though I were there . . . meseemeth even that afar off. . . .

[A fiery glow spreads like dust in the atmosphere; the lands are lifted, and the sand disappears slowly beneath the grass.]

" And it was told to Tamar, saying, Behold thy father-in-law goeth up to Timnath to shear his sheep." . . .

[Great mountains outline their blue scalloped peaks against a violet sky.   There are tents on the hills and flocks of black sheep : one can hear the cry of the shepherds ; and the bells tinkle. S. Anthony, as he continues reading, sees facing him two paths that cross one another. A woman comes up and sits down by the way-side.   Her eyeballs gleam in the rift of her white veil that passes several times about her face, raising the tips of her ears and keeping her big gold earrings clear of her head.   The breeze presses her summer robing against her body, and the garment is shaken behind her and claps in the air like a flag.   A shepherd comes forward, clad in a yellow cloak that is fastened round his forehead by a brass circlet. He carries a stick with a crook to it, and he walks with dignity in his goatskin sandals. He approaches her—they are face to face—they speak in a low voice ; the man draws from off his finger a silver signet, and from his head the brass circlet, and lays down his staff ; the woman puts the signet ring on her finger and the circlet on her arm ; she takes the staff and says :]

At once ! There ! . . .

THE SHEPHERD.   Nay, the goat's dung will spoil thy fine robe.

[They go further off, and the shepherd speaks again.] Surely there is some forgotten cistern somewhere at hand. . . .

THE WOMAN.   Thou art foolish as a child, thou shepherd with the long beard !

THE SHEPHERD. [Laughing.] Thou art a merry maid ! I would fain see thy face.

THE WOMAN. [She looks frightened.] Nay, nay !
[She crouches down, her yellow robe is caught by the fringe in the thorns; the sun becomes so strong and so luminous that they vanish in a dazzling light. The rocks crack, the grass bursts into flame, and the whole valley smokes as though it were covered with craters. Great clouds glide over the sky, like huge purple veils borne away by the wind.]

S. ANTHONY. [Gasping, lets fall the Bible.] Ah me ! I am athirst ! My flesh burneth !
[All disappears, and in the slanting light of the moon is seen a clear lake that loses itself beneath tree-trunks. The thick roots standing out of the water are covered with moss. The higher branches above bow them to a dome; and here and there pierces a greenish ray of daylight that sparkles upon the leaves, shivers at the tips of the blades of grass, glitters against the pebbles, and casts lengthening ribbons of changing light over the wet sand. Hanging white vapours rend apart slowly; the dew trickles down the bark of the trees; one great willow-tree stretches across everything, from one side to the other, with one spray that falls back.]
Ah, how pleasant is it ! It raineth ! I hear the drops . . . and my breast is opened to the sweet smells of the green things . . . even as, aforetime in my youth, when I ran upon the mountains, chasing the lightfooted stags . . . [He falls into a reverie] and the voice of the hounds came unto me with the sound of the torrents and the murmur of the leaves.
[Two coupled greyhounds push their noses through the branches, pulling the while on their leash that is held on the finger of a young woman clad in a short-skirted robe. She walks quickly and looks behind her. A little quiver is beating against her

G

back. The freshness of the morning has flushed
to rose her oval face crowned with brown damp
tresses. She throws down her arrows and her bow
on the lawn, then quiets her hounds and ties them
up to a privet-bush, then, standing on one foot only,
she begins to undo the latchet of her Cretan shoe.]
Waters of fire run beneath my flesh—longing to live
getteth hold on me. All my being roareth! I am
an-hungered, I thirst!

THEY TAKE OFF THEIR VESTURE.

[S. Anthony moves forward. Other women run up.
They take off their vesture and hang it to the
branches of the trees. They shiver, they enter the
water, feeling it with their feet, throwing it into
their faces. They laugh—S. Anthony laughs.
They bend down—he bends down.]
Aha! rejoice, praise be unto mirth! I dabble, I drink,
I am happy, I need but a well-served table! . . .
[Then appears, beneath a black sky, a vast hall, lit
with golden candlesticks.

Plinths of porphyry, supporting columns that are half lost in the shadow, so high are they, form long lines, one following the other, outside the tables that lengthen out even to the horizon where appear, in a luminous mist, enormous structures, pyramids, cupolae, stairways, flights of steps—arcades with colonnades and obelisks upon domes. Between the silver-footed bronze couches and the long pitchers whence streams forth black wine, choirs of musicians crowned with violets pluck at great harps and sing in vibrant voices; at the far end, above the rest, alone, crowned with the tiara, and robed in scarlet, the King Nebuchadnezzar eats and drinks. Behind him a colossal statue, fashioned in his image, stifles nations in its arms; on the head of it is a diadem of hollow stones that hold lamps and cast blue rays of light all round it.

At the four corners of his table are four priests in white mantles and pointed bonnets, holding censers the smoke of whose incense they swing about him. On the ground below him crawl the captive kings, footless and handless; he throws them food; yet lower down stand his brethren, their eyes bandaged, for they are blind, every one of them.

Slaves run about with dishes, women pass round the tables and pour out for the guests to drink, the baskets creak for the weight of the loaves, a dromedary comes and goes, laden with pierced wine-skins whence flows vervain to freshen the pavement. The knives glimmer, the flowers drop their petals, the pyramids of fruit collapse, the candles burn.

Laughing beast-tamers lead in lions who growl. Dancing girls, their hair held in nets, turn on their hands, spitting fire through their nostrils. Negro mountebanks juggle, naked children pelt one another with snowballs that smash as they fall against the shining silver vessels. The cymbals clash, the king drinks. He wipes the perfumes from his face with his arm. He eats out of the sacred vessels. He rolls his eyes.

So great is the multitude that the sound of it is as the sea! A cloud floats over the feast, so countless are the meats and so countless the breath of men! Now and again a flake flies from off the great torches, snatched away by the wind, and crosses the hall like a shooting-star.

All of a sudden appears a man clad in goat-skins. The king falls from his throne, the columns and their capitals are overthrown like trees, the dishes clash together like waves of gold, all rise to their feet, and no more can be seen but the backs of those that flee.

S. Anthony finds himself once more in front of his hut. It is broad daylight.]

What! . . . the sun is shining! Yet a moment past I was in deep night! Yet this is indeed mine own hut, and this is mine own self of a surety. [He touches himself.] This is my body! These be mine hands! My heart beateth; and the pig is yet here . . . he lyeth on the sand, and the froth is at his mouth. Nay, nay! Bethink we! I am alone! No one hath come hither, of that am I sure!

[But he sees facing him three riders mounted on wild asses, clad in green robes, holding lilies in their hands; they all three resemble one another in countenance. They do not move—neither do the wild asses; these lower their long ears, and stretch forth their necks, they draw back their lips and show their gums.

S. Anthony turns round; he sees yet three other riders, similar to these, on similar asses, and in the same posture. He draws back. Then the wild asses, all at the same time, go one pace forward and rub their muzzles against him, trying to bite his vesture.

There is a sound of tomtoms and little bells, and a great clamour of voices crying out "Hither, hither . . . this is the place."

Banners appear between the clefts of the mountain, and heads of camels with red silken halters, and mules laden with baggage, and women, covered with yellow veils, riding astride on piebald horses. The panting beasts lie down. The slaves rush to the bales and untie the knots of the cords with their teeth. They unroll motley carpets, they spread glittering things upon the ground.

Arrives a white elephant, caparisoned in a golden net, shaking the tuft of ostrich feathers bound to his frontal. On his back, amidst blue woollen cushions, her legs crossed, her eyelids half closed, her head swaying, is a woman so splendidly attired that she sends forth rays on all sides of her; behind her, on the crupper, standing on one foot, is a negro, red-booted and with coral bracelets; he holds in his hand a great round leaf with which he fans her, grinning the while.

The crowd fall on their faces, the elephant bends his knees, and the Queen of Sheba, letting herself slide adown his shoulder, descends on to the carpets and advances towards S. Anthony.

Her gown is of gold brocade, divided at regular intervals by furbelows of pearls, of jet, and of sapphires; her waist is held in by its strait bodice that is adorned with applied designs in colour representing the twelve signs of the Zodiac. She has very high-heeled pattens, the one of which is black, sown with silver stars and a crescent moon, while the other, which is white, is covered with tiny drops of gold with a sun in the middle.

Her large sleeves, ornate with emeralds and birds'

feathers, show naked her little round arms adorned
at the wrists with ebony bracelets, and her hands,
loaded with rings, end in nails so pointed that
the tips of her fingers look almost like needles.
A chain of flat gold, passing under her chin and
up her cheeks, winds in spirals round her high
head-dress powdered with blue powder, then,
falling again, grazes her shoulders and passes to

AN APE HOLDS THE END OF IT.

her bosom, fastened thereupon to a little diamond
scorpion whose tongue protrudes between her breasts.
Two big white pearls pull down her ears. The
edges of her eyelids are painted with black. She
has a brown patch on her left cheek-bone; she
opens her mouth when she breathes, as though
her bodice constrained her.
As she walks, she shakes a green parasol, ivory-
handled, hung round with vermilion bells; twelve
frizzled little nigger boys bear the long train of
her beautiful gown, and an ape holds the end of

it; he lifts it up from time to time to peep there-
under.]

THE QUEEN OF SHEBA. Ah, fair hermit, fair hermit!
My heart faileth me!

S. ANTHONY. [Drawing back.] Begone! Thou art
a vision! I know it! Get thee behind me!

THE QUEEN OF SHEBA. For my impatient stamping
mine heels have grown hard, and I have broken one of
my nails. I sent forth shepherds who stood upon the
mountains and held their hands before their eyes. I sent
forth hunters who cried thy name aloud in the woods,
I sent forth spies who went over all highways and asked
of every one that passed by: " Hast thou seen him ? "
At last, at even, I came down from my tower; nay,
rather, mine handmaids bore me away in their arms, for
I swooned daily when the Dog-star rose.

S. ANTHONY. [To himself.] In vain do I close mine
eyelids, yet do I see her ever! . . .

THE QUEEN OF SHEBA. They brought back the life
to me by burning herbs, and they put into my mouth,
with an iron spoon, an Indian sweetmeat that hath this
virtue that it maketh kings happy; so much thereof did
I swallow that the itch of it is yet in my throat, deep down.
I passed my nights with my face turned to the wall, and
I wept! My tears, after many days, made two small holes
in the pavement, as it were pools of sea-water in the
rocks. For I love thee . . . yea, I love thee greatly!

[She takes hold of his beard.]

Laugh, fair hermit, laugh! I am very merry, thou shalt
see it! I play upon the lute. I dance like unto a bee. I
know many many tales to tell, the one more pleasant
than the other.

How shalt thou know how long a way we have come!
The hooves of the camels are worn; behold the wild
asses of my green riders! they are dead for weariness!

[S. Anthony looks, and indeed the asses are stretched
on the ground motionless.]

Since three long moons have they run at unchanged speed, holding a pebble in their teeth wherewith to cut the wind, their tails ever stretched straight, their hams ever folded, galloping without ceasing !   Never shall man find again their likes !   They were mine from my mother's father, the great King Saharil, the son of Iakhschab, the son of Iaarab, the son of Kastan.   Ah, did they yet live, we would harness them unto a litter that we might return swiftly unto mine house.   But . . . how ? . . . whereon thinkest thou ?   [She looks carefully at him.] Ah !   When thou art wedded unto me, I will clothe thee, I will perfume thee with sweet odours, I will pluck out the hairs of thy body.

> [S. Anthony stands motionless, stiffer than a stake, pale as a dead man, his eyes wide open.]

Thou art sad of countenance !   Wherefore then ?   Is it for leaving thine hut ?   Yet have I left all for thee—even unto the King Solomon, though he hath much wisdom, and twenty thousand chariots of war, and a long beard ! I have brought thee my wedding gifts.   Choose thou therefrom !

> [She walks through the ranks of slaves and merchandise.]

Here is balm of Gennesareth, and incense from the Cape Gardefan ; here is gum and cinnamon, and silfy which is good to put into sauces.   Therein yonder are embroidered cloths of Asshur, and ivory from the Ganges, and purple of Elisa ; in this box of snow is a wine-skin of the wine of Chalibon that is for the kings of Assyria alone ; they drink it pure in the horn of an unicorn.   Here be necklaces, clasps, nets, parasols ; here is powder of gold of Bashan, and tin from Tartessus, blue wood from Pandion, white furs from Issedonia, carbuncles from the isle of Palaesimond, and toothpicks made of the hairs of the tachas—he is lost, he dwelleth beneath the earth.   These cushions are from Emath and these fringes of mantles from Palmyra.   Upon this carpet, of

Babylon, there is . . . but come thou hither! Nay,
come!

    [She pulls S. Anthony by the sleeve. He resists.
    She continues :]

Yonder fine woof that crackleth in the fingers with the
crackle of sparks of fire, is the wondrous yellow cloth
that is brought by the merchants of Bactria. They need
forty and three interpreters for their journey. I will
have robes made thereof for thee and thou shalt put
them on in mine house.

Push the hasps of the sycamore casket and give me the
ivory box that is on the garrot of my elephant.

    [Her servants draw from a box something round
    covered with a skin, and they bring her a little
    casket covered with chased work.]

Wouldest thou the buckler of Djian-ben-Djian who
builded the Pyramids? Lo! Here it is! It is fashioned
of seven skins of dragons, set the one over the other,
jointed by screws of diamond, tanned in the gall of sons
that slew their fathers. On the one side it sheweth
forth all the wars that were since weapons of war were
made known, and on the other are all the wars that
shall be, even unto the end of the world. The thunder-
bolt leapeth up from off it as it were a ball of cork. If
thou art brave, thou shalt put it upon thine arm and
wear it when thou goest forth to the chase. Ah! Didst
thou but know what I have in my little box! Turn it
over! Assay to open it! None may compass that. Kiss
me and I will tell thee.

    [She takes S. Anthony's cheeks between her two
    hands; he pushes her back with outstretched arms.]

It was upon a night wherein the King Solomon lost his
wit for desire of me. In the end we made a barter.
He rose and went out stealthily. . . .

                  [She turns a pirouette.]

Ha! Fair hermit! Thou shalt not know it! Thou
shalt not know!

x) p. xov

[She shakes her parasol and all its little bells ring.]

Ay, many more things have I! I have treasures shut up in galleries where men are lost as in a wood. I have summer palaces woven in trellis of reeds, and winter palaces built of black marble. In the midst of lakes, great as seas, I have islands round as pieces of silver, wholly covered with the shell of the pearl, whose shores give forth music to the beating of the warm tides that roll toward the sand. The slaves of my kitchen take birds in my cages and catch fish in my vivers. I have gravers who sit continually graving mine image upon hard stones, I have smelters who pant for breath and cast statues of me, I have perfumers who mingle the sap of plants with vinegar and who beat out pastes, I have sewing women who cut vesture for me, and jewellers who work jewel work for me, I have tire-women who seek new tirings for my hair, and careful painters, who pour upon my wainscoting boiling gums that they cool with fans. The women of my following are sufficient for a king's household, and my eunuchs are an army. I have armed hosts, I have peoples! I have in mine antechamber a bodyguard of dwarfs who bear upon their backs horns of ivory.

[S. Anthony sighs.]

I have gazelles harnessed, I have double yokes of elephants, and coupled camels by hundreds, I have mares whose manes are so long that their hooves are caught therein when they gallop; furthermore, I have herds of oxen whose horns are so great that men hew down the woods before them when they are at pasture. I have giraffes that walk in my gardens, that stretch forth their heads upon the edge of my roof what time I take the air after that I have supped.

Seated in a shell drawn by dolphins, I pass through the caverns. I listen to the fall of the water from the stalactites. I go into the land of diamonds where the magicians who are my friends leave the fairest for my choice : then I go up again on the earth and I enter again into mine own house.

[She pouts her lips and utters a shrill whistle, and a great bird descends from the sky and settles upon the top of her head-dress and scatters the blue powder therefrom. His orange-coloured plumage looks as though it were made of metal scales. His little head surmounted with a silver tuft has a human face. He has four wings, he has vulture's claws, he has an immense peacock's tail which he spreads out in a round behind him. He takes the Queen's parasol in his beak, then totters a little before he attains his balance, then bristles all his feathers and remains motionless.]

I thank thee, fair Simorg-Anka ! Thou who hast taught me where my lover was hid. Thanks be unto thee, messenger of mine heart !

He flieth like unto desire. He goeth the round of the world in his journey. In the evening he returneth and standeth at the foot of my couch ; he telleth unto me all that he hath seen ; he telleth of the seas that passed under him, the fish, and the ships, the great barren deserts, whereon he hath looked down from high heaven ; he telleth all the harvests that bowed them in the fields and the plants that grew upon the walls of deserted cities.

[She passes her arm languidly round S. Anthony's neck.]

Ah ! Didst thou but wish it ! Didst thou wish . . . I have a pavilion upon an headland in the middle of a passage between two seas. It is wainscoted with plates of glass, the floor thereof is of the scales of tortoises, and it is open unto the four winds of heaven.

From on high I see my fleets return and the folk climbing the hill with their burdens upon their shoulders. We should sleep upon coverlets softer than

clouds, we should drink cool drink in cups of the rind
of fruits, and we should look upon the sun through
windows of emerald!   Come!

[The Simorg-Anka makes the glittering eyes of his
tail turn like wheels, and the Queen of Sheba sighs.]

SO BEAUTIFUL A WOMAN!

Ah me!   I die!   I die!   [S. Anthony bows his head.]
Ah!   Thou dost spurn me! . . . Farewell!

[She moves away weeping. The procession sets
forth; S. Anthony looks at her; she stops.]

Art thou indeed resolved?   So beautiful a woman!
That hath a tuft of hair between her breasts!

[She laughs. The ape that holds the end of her robe lifts it with outstretched arms and leaps up and down.]

Thou wilt repent, fair hermit! Thou wilt groan, thou wilt be weary. But I mock thereat! Aha! Aha! Ho! Ho!

[She goes away, her face in her hands, hopping. The slaves pass in the line before S. Anthony, the horses, the dromedaries, the elephant, the women of the Queen's following, the mules who have been reloaded, the little negro boys, the ape, the green riders holding in their hands their lilies, broken, and the Queen of Sheba departs, uttering a species of convulsive hiccup that is like a sob or maybe a cackle. But her trailing robe that lengthens out behind her as she advances, arrives like a tide even to S. Anthony's sandals. He puts his foot upon it; all disappears.]

S. ANTHONY. What have I done? Wretched man that I am!   [He laments.]

Ah me! How shall I free me from the vision that continually persecuteth me? The pebbles of the wilderness, the bitter water that I drink, the hair-cloth that I wear, all these do change for my damnation into painted pavements, into floods of wine, into mantles of purple. Through my desire I do roll me in the whoredoms of the Chief cities, and repentance escapeth from my strivings as it were an handful of sand that slippeth between the fingers, close I mine hand never so tightly. This above all things doth anger me, that this my countless enemy fleeth ever! Where shall he be found?

                    [Rage seizes him.]

I will plunge deep into awful imaginations. I will mortify myself and compel my thoughts to fasten on sadness, seeing that repentance sufficeth not; I will search out suffering with my mind.

Yet would I love better suffering of the body, were it

even beyond bearing! Yea, sooner would I wrestle
with savage beasts, and behold my flesh fly apart as it
were a red fruit at the edge of a sword! Ay, better
would I love that! That would I welcome!

[Suddenly he perceived the interior of a tower.
It is pierced by an embrasure that cuts out a narrow
square of blue sky far up in the darkness of the
wall; through this embrasure flows a thin stream
of sand, noiselessly, ceaselessly, so that little by
little it fills the tower.

On the ground are grey masses of strange shape,
vague as ruined statues. There is as it were a
trembling movement throughout them, and at length
S. Anthony discerns that they are men, all seated
on the ground, their two arms resting on their
knees, their fists under their armpits; in their
right hands they hold knives; their attitude is
savage and despairing. They raise their heads
slowly. Their locks and the hair of their beards
are white with dust, their eyeballs are yellow, their
cheek-bones are sharp, and their nostrils are edged
with black, like those of men about to die. They
come, one after the other, dragging themselves
along, they strike all at the same spot against the
stones of the wall, then they let fall again their
great lean arms that are like dried-up vine-stocks.

But a rat passes swiftly through their midst. They
fling themselves upon it with their knives;
S. Anthony can distinguish no more, so furious
becomes the medley. He sees them again, all
huddled in a circle before a mutilated corpse from
which they tear great strips with their hands.
Pearly red drops sweat upon the wall. Their eyes
roll terribly, their teeth clash together like the
steel of sickles that meet, and S. Anthony hears
them mutter: "Our fathers have eaten of the sour
grapes and the teeth of the children are set on

edge." But the sand that falls through the embrasure heaps up around them, and rises even to their shoulders : they repeat, "Our fathers have eaten of the sour grapes and the teeth of the children are set on edge." The sand rises to their lips, to their eyes, to their foreheads. Only the tops of their heads appear. Then all is covered up and not a sound more is heard.]

Horror ! [He takes his head in both hands.] Oh ! My head, my head ! What shall I do that I may tear from out thereof that which filleth it ? How shall I know whether in very truth I have seen these things that I have seen ?

Were they indeed things . . . there would be union therein, and reason for their being . . . nay, nay ! I deceive myself ! . . . but I do indeed see them ! They are yonder before me ! I touch them ! Nay, but it cannot be, it cannot be !

Meseemeth that what is without entereth into me, nay, rather, my thought goeth out like the lightning from a cloud and of itself putteth upon it a body, even here, before mine eyes ! Peradventure, thus did God, in thought, devise the creation ? Is it not more real than some one of these visions that dazzle mine eyes ? But wherefore be they visions ? Know I even what is a vision ? Whereof is truth of things ? Where doth the truth begin, and where doth vision end ? A tide within a tide, clouds in the night-time, the wind in the wind ; and after these, as it were, uncertain currents that whirl, that drive me, changing shapes without end, that rise, that fall, that are lost.

Ha ! I can discern nought ; but meseemeth two great beasts are here ? The one crawleth, the other hovereth . . . O God ! They draw nigh unto me !

[Athwart the twilight appears the Sphinx. He stretches out his paws, he slowly shakes the fillets that are upon his brow, and he crouches flat upon his belly.

Leaping, flying, spitting fire through his nostrils,
beating his wings with his dragon's tail, the Chimera,
green-eyed, circles and bays. The ringlets of his
tresses, cast to one side, mingle with the hairs on his
loins; on the other side they hang down even upon
the sand and sway to the swing of his whole body.]
THE SPHINX. [Motionless, looking at the Chimera.]
Hither, Chimera, stay thee!
THE CHIMERA. Nay! never!

SPITTING FIRE THROUGH HIS NOSTRILS.

THE SPHINX. Run not so swiftly, fly not so high, bay
not so loud!
THE CHIMERA. Call no more upon me! Call me no
more! Forasmuch as thou art ever dumb, never dost
thou move.
THE SPHINX. Nay, cease thou from casting flame
into my face, from howling into my ears! Thou shalt
never melt the stone of me, thou shalt not open my
lips.
THE CHIMERA. Neither shalt thou seize hold of me,

thou terrible Sphinx, who dost flash thy great eye, everlasting, unto the land's end.

THE SPHINX. Thou art too mad that thou shouldest abide with me.

THE CHIMERA. And thou art too heavy that thou shouldest follow me.

THE SPHINX. This long time have I seen thy twain unfolded wings glide in the tempest at the edge of the wilderness.

THE CHIMERA. This long time have I galloped over the sand and seen thine austere countenance darkening in the sun.

THE SPHINX. In the night-time, when I pass through the corridors of the labyrinth, when I hear the wind roaring under the galleries where passeth the moon, I hear the sound of thy frail feet upon the ringing pavement. Whither goest thou that thou dost flee so swiftly? . . . I, even I, remain at the foot of the stairway, I gaze at the stars in the basons of porphyry.

THE CHIMERA. Air! Air! Fire! Fire! I run upon the waves, I hover upon the mountains, I bay in the gulfs. With my trailing tail I sweep the shores of the sea. When I did lay me down upon the earth, my belly dug out valleys, and the hills have rounded their shape according to the mould of my shoulders. But thou, thou dost ever crouch, thou dost growl like unto the storm, ever again I find thee unmoved, or, it may be, scribing letters upon the sand with thy claw.

THE SPHINX. Ay, I keep my secret. I ponder. I reckon in numbers. The ocean swayeth yet in his great bed; the jackal whineth near the sepulchres; the ears of corn bow them ever to the same wind. I see the dust awhirl and the sun shining, I hear the breathing of the wind.

THE CHIMERA. I am light of heart, I am cheerful. I discover unto men dazzling visions, paradise in the clouds, happiness afar off. I pour endless madness

H

into their souls, plans of blessedness, thoughts of the days to come, dreams of glory, sworn oaths withal of love, and righteous resolves.

I have builded strange buildings whose adornments I have graven with the nail of my claw. I it was who did hang bells upon the tomb of Porsenna. I, even I, discovered idols four-armed, worship without shame, proud tirings of the hair.

I urge the mariners unto journeys of great venture; in the mist they see the islands with green pastures, and domes and naked women that dance; they smile for all the ravishments that do sing within their soul, in the midst of the great billows that close in upon the ship that is foundered.

[S. Anthony walks to and fro between the two great beasts whose jowls graze his shoulders.]

THE SPHINX. O Phantasy, phantasy! Bear me away on thy wings that I may be freed of my sadness!

THE CHIMERA. O Unknown, Unknown! My desire is to thine eyes! As a rutting hyena, so do I go about thee. I beseech gendering of thee, the need of it eateth me up.

Open thy jaws! Lift up thy feet! Get thee upon my back!

THE SPHINX. Since that my feet have been flat upon the earth they can no more be raised. The lichen hath grown upon my mouth as it were a sore. For very pondering I have no word more to say.

THE CHIMERA. Thou liest, thou hypocrite! I have seen thine hidden manhood! Wherefore callest thou ever upon me, yet ever deniest me?

THE SPHINX. Nay, it is thou, untamed Waywardness, that dost pass and turn as it were a whirlwind.

THE CHIMERA. Shalt thou blame me? . . . How? . . . Leave me!   [He bays :] Houaho! Houaho!

THE SPHINX. Thou movest, thou dost escape me!
                    [He growls :] Heoum, eum!

THE CHIMERA. Shall we make trial? . . . thou doest crush me! Houaho, Houaho!

[The Chimera bays, the Sphinx growls, monstrous butterflies hum, lizards advance, bats flit, frogs leap, caterpillars crawl, great spiders crawl about.]

THE PIG. Pity on me! These fearful beasts will devour me raw!

S. ANTHONY. I am a-cold! Terror unbounded entereth into me! Methinks I see as it were wandering shapes who search for substance, or, maybe, beings created that dissolve into thoughts! They are as the gaze of an eye that passeth, as limbs unshapen that quiver, mortal appearances more transparent than bubbles of air.

THE MOUTHLESS FOLK. Breathe not too lustily! Raindrops crush us, false sounds blind us, darkness teareth us asunder. We are made of wind, of perfume, of rays of light, we are a little more than dreams, we are not wholly beings.

THE HALF-FOLK. We have but one eye, one cheek, one nostril, one hand, one leg, the half of a body, the half of an heart; we dwell wholly at our ease in our houses that are but half a house, with our half-wives and our halves of children.

THE SHADE-FOOTED FOLK. We are bound to the earth by our locks that are longer than the bindweed. We lie in the shadow of our feet that are wide as parasols, and we look athwart these upon the light of day, and our veins that intertwine one with another, and our roseate blood that goeth around in its course.

THE BLEMMYES. We have no heads and our shoulders are the broader thereby; there is no ox nor rhinoceros nor elephant who may bear what we bear. The dim likeness of a face and the similitude of the parts thereof are printed upon our breasts; that is all! Our stomach is a thought, our humours are an imagination. The God who is our God floateth in peace in the innermost chyles.

We walk straight upon our way, we pass through all
sloughs, we go warily by all gulfs ; of all people we toil
the most ; we are the happiest, the most righteous.

THE PIGMIES. We little mannikins do swarm upon
the world even as the lice upon the hump of a dromedary. Men burn us, they drown us, they crush us, yet
ever we appear again with fuller life, and in greater
number, terrible for the multitude of us.

THE DOG-HEADED FOLK [An hairy people who
live in the woods in disordered wise]. We climb into
the trees that we may suck the eggs of birds, we pluck
the nestlings, and we put their nests as it were a bonnet
upon our heads. Woe unto the virgin who goeth alone
unto the fountain !

Up and on, my fellows ! Let us gnash our white teeth,
shake we the boughs !

S. ANTHONY. Who is this doth breathe in my face
this odour of sap whereat my heart fainteth ? [He sees]

THE SADHUZAG [A great black stag with the head
of a bull, bearing between his ears a bush of white
horns].

My three score and twelve antlers are hollow even
as flutes. I bow them and I straighten them . . .
behold !

                [He swings his horns backwards and forwards.]
When I turn me toward the south wind, a sound goeth
forth from them that draweth unto me all beasts ravished.
The serpents twine about my legs, the wasps cling to
my nostrils, the parrots and the doves and the ibis perch
upon my branches . . . listen !

        [He throws back his horns, and a wondrous music
            unspeakable goes out from them.]

S. ANTHONY. What sounds are these ! My heart is
loosened ! It trembleth ! This music shall surely
bear my heart away with it !

THE SADHUZAG. But when I turn me to the north,
and bend my horns, that are more tufted than a bat-

talion of spears, there goeth out therefrom a terrible voice, and the forests tremble; the lotus bursteth into flower, the waterfalls turn them back unto their sources, the earth doth shake for fear, and the blades of grass bristle, even as the hair on the head of a fearful man . . . hearken !

> [He bows his antlers forward, and from them goes forth a music of fear.]

S. ANTHONY. Ah me ! I am dissolved, and all that is in mine head is torn therefrom and doth whirl round even as the leaves of a tree in a great wind !

THE UNICORN. [Caracoling before him.] Gallop ! Gallop ! I have hooves of ivory, and teeth of steel, my head is the colour of purple and my body is white as snow, the horn in my forehead is white at the base and black in the middle and red at the end of it.

I travel from Chaldaea into the wilderness of Tartary, upon the banks of the Ganges and in Mesopotamia. I outrun the ostriches; I run so swiftly that I draw the wind with me. I rub my back against the palm-trees. I roll among the cane trees. With one leap I leap over rivers, and when I pass through Persepolis, it is my sport to break with mine horn the faces of the kings that are graven upon the mountain.

THE GRIFFIN [A lion with an eagle's beak, white-winged; his body is black and his neck blue]. I, even I, do know the caverns where the old kings lie asleep ! They are seated upon their thrones, they are crowned with tiaras and robed in red mantles; a chain that cometh out of the wall doth hold their heads straight, and their sceptres of emerald are laid upon their knees. Near unto them in basons of porphyry the women that they have loved float, white-robed, upon black water. Their treasures are stored in the halls, in stacks whose shape is that of a diamond, in heaps and in pyramids. There be bars longer than the masts of ships, there be cages filled with diamonds, there be suns fashioned of carbuncles.

I stand on the hoary hills, my hinder parts are against the door of the cavern, my claws are lifted up high; with my flaming eyes I spy out them that would come. It is a pale land, full of precipices, without life, a land ravaged. The black sky is spread over the valley wherein the bones of the wayfarers crumble into dust. . . . I will lead thee thither, O Anthony, and the doors shall open of themselves; thou shalt smell the hot steam of the mines, thou shalt go down into the passages under the earth.

S. ANTHONY. Nay, nay! It is as though the earth did crush me! I stifle. . . .

[He lifts his forehead towards heaven.]

THE PHŒNIX. [Hovering, pauses; he has great wings of gold, rays go forth from his eyes.] I cross the firmaments, I raze the beaches where I peck at the stars as I pass; I hop on the tips of my claws upon the Milky Way as it were an hen that hoppeth amid grains of oats.

When I would sleep, I lie me down in the moon, I bend my body unto the curved shape of her. At other times I take her in my beak, and with mighty strokes of my wings I draw her through the Heavens. Then it is that she runneth so swiftly, she goeth down into the valleys she leapeth over the brooks, she skippeth above the woods, even as a kid that wandereth in the great blue plain.

But when the flame of the suns can no longer warm my blood for that it hath grown thin, I go into the land of Arabia to seek fresh myrrh whereof I build me a nest for my burial. Then do I close my wings and make me ready to die.

The rain of the equinox that falleth upon mine ashes doth mingle them with the perfume that is still warm. A worm cometh forth, wings grow upon him, he taketh flight; he is the Phœnix, the son, raised again to life, from the father. New stars flower forth, a younger sun blazeth into light, and the idle worlds begin again to turn them.

> [The Phœnix flies about in flaming circles; S. Anthony, dazzled, lowers his eyes towards the earth, and other animals appear, horned beasts, deep-bellied monsters.]

THE PIG. I am sick! Ah! How I suffer! They torment me! Woe, woe, woe, woe is me! [He runs hither and thither.] I am burned, choked, strangled! I die in all wise! My tail is pulled, my belly is pinched, my back is flayed, an asp biteth my genitals.

S. ANTHONY. Woe is me for my pig!

THE BASILISK. [A gigantic serpent, violet-hued, with three-lobed crest, advances, erect to heaven.] Beware! Thou wilt fall into my jaws! I am He that devoureth all things, I am the son of the burning mountains, I have been suckled on lava and fed upon sulphur! The rocks whereon I alight do burst, the trees that my coils do enfold are enkindled into flame, ice melteth at my look; when I pass through the burial fields, the bones of the dead leap in their graves, as it were chestnuts within an oven. I have drunk of the dew of the pastures, of the sap of plants, of the blood of beasts. I drink fire, fire draweth me unto him! I would swallow thy marrow, I would suck thine heart dry. I have two teeth, the one above, the other below, thou shalt feel the bite of them!

> [The serpents hiss, the wild beasts bark, jaws clash, there is rain of drops of blood.]

THE MANTICHORA [A lion, the colour of cinnabar, with a human face; he has three rows of red teeth, a scorpion's tail, and green eyes].

I run after men. I seize them by the reins, and I beat their heads against the mountains that their brains may gush forth. I sweat pestilence. I spit hail. I it is who devour armies when they adventure into the wilderness.

My nails are twisted into augurs, my teeth are shaped like saws, and my tail, that I raise and let fall and turn round, bristleth with darts that I fling to the right, to the left, in front, behind . . . Lo! Lo!

> [The Mantichora flings the quills from his tail in successive streaks. S. Anthony, motionless in the midst of the animals, stands listening to all those voices and gazing upon all those shapes.]

THE DOWNLOOKER [A black buffalo with a pig's head that droops to the ground and is joined to his shoulders by a lean long neck, flabby as an empty gut. His belly touches the earth at every point, and his feet disappear beneath the enormous mane of hard hairs that covers his face].

Thus do I ever stay, gross, melancholy, fierce, ever I feel the heat of the earth under my belly.

So heavy is my head that I cannot bear it up, I roll it about me slowly; I open my jaw, and I tear up with my tongue poisonous herbs that are watered with my breath. Once I did even devour mine own feet, nor was I aware of it.

No man hath ever seen mine eyes, O Anthony; nay, they that have seen them are dead. Did I lift my swollen red eyelids, at once thou wouldst die.

S. ANTHONY. Ah! Yonder beast! . . .

Were I then to desire to look upon those eyes! Verily, his fierce witlessness draweth me thereunto, I tremble! I am drawn on I know not how toward depths full of fear, nor can I resist!

> [He sees advancing sea-urchins, dolphins, fishes that walk upright upon their beards, great oysters yawning, cuttle-fish spouting forth black liquid, whales blowing water through their blow-holes, horns of ammonites unrolling like cables, and sea-grey four-footed beasts that sway damp seaweed upon their heads. Green phosphorescence glistens about their fins, at the edge of their gills, on the

crest of their backs, encircling round valves, cling-
ing to the moustaches of the seals, or trailing along
the ground, like long lines of emeralds that cross
one another.]

THE BEASTS OF THE SEA. [Breathing noisily.]
The sand of the way hath fouled our scales and we open
our mouths as it were dogs out of breath.

We will take thee, O Anthony, thou shalt come with us
upon beds of wrack, through plains of coral that quiver
to the ordered movement of deep billows. Thou knowest not our great waters. Many peoples dwell in the
countries of the ocean. Some shelter them from the
tempests. Others swim in the open sea, in the trans-
parency of the cold waves, breathing through their
trunks the water of the tides that ebb, or bearing
upon their shoulders the burden of the sources of the
sea. There be plants, wholly round, like unto carven
suns that shelter sleeping animals. Their limbs grow
with the rocks. The dim blue shell-fish doth quiver
throughout its slothful body even as a flood of azure.

No sound hear we save the unceasing murmur of the
great waters, and above our heads we watch the passing
of the keels of the ships as it were black stars gliding in
silence.

S. ANTHONY. Ah, me! I can no longer discern. . . .
[And as S. Anthony considers the beasts, yet more
fearful and monstrous creatures arrive; the Trage-
laphus, half-stag and half-bull; the Phalmant,
blood-coloured, who bursts his belly by the might
of his howling; the great weasel Pastinaca, who
kills trees by his stink; the Senad, three-headed,
who tears his young with his tongue; the Myrme-
coleo, lion in front and ant behind, whose genitals
are reversed; the serpent Aksar, whose length is
sixty cubits, he who frightened Moses; the dog
Cepus whose teats distil blue colour; the Porphyrus
whose saliva gives death in transports of lascivious-

1) Illustration on p. 106

ness; the Presteros, whose touch kills the understanding; the Mirag, a horned hare who dwells
in the islands of the sea.

On a sudden arrive raging whirlwinds full of
wondrous forms. There are heads of alligators
upon feet of roe-deer, horses' necks that end in
vipers, frogs hairy as bears, owls with serpents'

MONSTROUS CREATURES ARRIVE.

tails, swine with tigers' jowls, goats with the croup
of a donkey, chameleons huge as hippopotami,
four-footed hens, and calves with two heads, the
one whereof weeps while the other bellows,
quadruple fœtera that hold to one another by the
navel and dance round like tops, clusters of bees
unthreading like rosaries, aloes all covered with
roseate pustules, winged paunches that hover
like gnats, bodies of women that have in place

of faces open lotus-flowers, gigantic carcases whose white joints creak shrilly; and vegetables whose sap beneath their rind throbs like blood, minerals whose facets gaze as it were eyes, polypi catching hold with their arms, contracting their sheaths, opening their pores, swelling out, increasing, advancing.

And those that have passed by return, those that are not yet come arrive. They fall from the sky, they come out of the earth, they slip down the rocks. The Dog-headed folk bark, the Shade-footed people lie down, the Blemmyes toil, the Pigmies squabble, the Mouthless Men sob, the Unicorn neighs, the Mantichora roars, the Griffin paws the ground, the Basilisk hisses, the Phœnix soars, the Sadhuzag gives forth sounds, the Downlooker sighs, the Chimera cries aloud, the Sphinx growls—the beasts of the sea begin to wave their fins, the reptiles breathe forth their venom, the frogs hop, the gnats hum; teeth clack, wings vibrate, breasts swell, claws lengthen out, flesh flaps. Some are bringing forth, others are mating, or devouring one another in one mouthful; heaped up, pressed together, stifling for the numbers of them, multiplying at contact, they climb the one upon the other. They rise in pyramids forming a complex mound of diverse bodies, each of which stirs with its own movement, while the whole oscillates, rustles, and glows through the air that is streaked with hail, snow, rain, lightning, wherein pass whirls of sand, spouts of wind, clouds of smoke, and it is lit at once by the beams of the moon, and the rays of the sun, and greenish twilight.]

S. ANTHONY. The blood of my veins heateth so mightily that it will burst them. My soul overfloweth within me. I would rush forth and flee afar without this place. For I too am a beast, life swarmeth within my belly. I long to fly in the air, to swim in the water, to run in the woods. Ah! How happy should I be, had I those stout lives under their hides that none may assail! How freely would I breathe, had I those wide-spreading wings!

I would fain bay, I would bellow, I would howl! I would live in a cavern and breathe forth smoke, I would bear a trunk, I would twist my body,—and divide me throughout, be in all things, go forth in odours, come to my fulness like the plants, be shaken like sound, shine like light, be blotted beneath shapes, enter into all atoms, move about within substance, be substance myself that I might know the thoughts thereof. . . .

THE DEVIL. [Swooping upon S. Anthony, catches him by the loins with his horns and bears him away with him, crying out.] Thou shalt know it! I will teach it unto thee!

THE PIG. [Reared up on his hind paws, watches S. Anthony disappear into space.] Ah! Wherefore have I not wings even as the pig of Clazomenae!

*) See note to p. 5, on p. 194

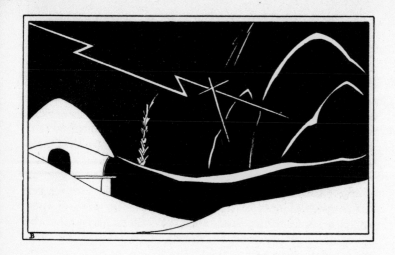

PART III

[In space.]

S. ANTHONY. [Clinging to the horns of the
Devil.] Whither go I?
THE DEVIL. [Crying out.] Higher, higher!
S. ANTHONY. The tops of the trees are lost
to sight. The hills sink! I strangle . . . the wind,
coming in great blasts, beateth my face.

THE DEVIL. Be of good courage! Leave not hold of
me!

S. ANTHONY. I float, lost in cold without end.
[The Devil still soars in wild wise; S. Anthony,
fainting, holds his seat between his horns.]

THE DEVIL. Now, open thine eyes!

S. ANTHONY. Ah, how broad is it! How fair is it! I
hear the murmur of the worlds. The stars fall without
noise, like snowflakes.

THE DEVIL. Seest thou down yonder a luminous
substance whence come forth suns?

S. ANTHONY. Ay, and the fragments that are loosed
therefrom are turned about and about!

THE DEVIL. So, without number and without end, do the souls stream forth unceasingly from the great soul. Further away, yonder golden dust that is spread abroad is but made of portions of quenched stars whose vanishing cometh to conclusion.

S. ANTHONY. Can the suns then be worn out?

THE DEVIL. Ay, the suns, but not the light that is in them! The shape perisheth, but the substance is eternal. When man dissolveth, when in one stroke that assembly of the moment is dispersed, then do all things whereof it was made depart in freedom, and worlds are ordained without ceasing . . . hast thou not discerned voices in the shaking of the reeds? The dogs that howl, do they not speak to thee of thy dead friends?

[Ever they rise.]

S. ANTHONY. How do we rise! What great space is this!

THE DEVIL. Ay, thou knewedst not that it was so great! Yet when thou didst move thine arm, didst thou know how thou didst move it? And when thy foot went forward, didst thou know wherefore it was? The dung of thy pig, powdering to dust in the sun, and the green beetles that did hum around it, sufficed, as though it were God, to torment thy thought, inasmuch as that which is infinitely small is no whit more easy of understanding than that which is infinitely great. But beyond the knowledge of men is there neither small nor great, for that which hath no bounds is beyond measure, eternity hath no period, God cannot be apportioned.

If the least jot or tittle of substance doth reveal unto thee as vast an horizon as the whole of all things, know that this is because there existeth in the one as in the other a gulf that none can bridge that maketh them one. Thus there are not two infinites, nor two Gods, nor two unities. He is, and beside Him is nought else!

THE DEVIL

S. ANTHONY. How shall this be? God is then in all
places? Then He is in the separation of them that
ponder, in the passion of them that suffer, in the doing
of them that do great deeds? In all this He aideth?
He is all this? . . . that part of me whereinto I never
had entrance, that then was God? Nay, let us rise,
higher, yet higher, even unto the end of all things!

[The firmament widens, the stars meet one another.]
THE DEVIL. Dost thou see the uncounted fires of
heaven, the constellations, the stars that fall and the
stars that live for tens of thousands of ages, and the
stars of one day? Each one of them doth turn, each
one of them doth shine, and thereof is the movement
the same and the light the same! The blood of man
beateth in his heart and swelleth out the veins of his
feet. The breath of God goeth among the worlds and
the happenings of the worlds, even as the drops of thy
blood, are wholly alike the one unto the other, even as
they are parts of the same whole and are themselves
made of yet other parts, and so shall it continue and so
shall it ever be. The breath that passeth even now
through thy nostrils is the manifold conclusion of a
thousand worlds created that have passed away and
are gone. The thought that cometh into thee hath been
led unto thee, in wanderings that are greater than is the
distance from thine eyes, even unto the last of these
stars. For whatsoever each man hath thought ever
since men were, that hath given of itself thereto, and
all substance and all spirit and all that hath appeared,
all that is, finite and infinite, shaping and thought, these
are bound together and confounded and do beget one
another.
Are there not things unmoving that are as animals,
souls that grow like the plants of the field, statues that
dream, lands that are as though they pondered? . . .
A mystical measure driveth all the atoms shaken
together, unto the dance unending—bodies, throughout

their life and their death, do but seek to enter again into the dust whence they came; the soul whose desire is unbounded hath but this hope that it may return unto God from whom it came.

S. ANTHONY. For this then is it that I have so often longed for death and sought to remember if I had not dwelt in other worlds.

THE DEVIL. Yet is not substance on the one side and spirit on the other; for then would there be an infinity of substance and an infinity of spirit, which is two infinities that would thereby be bounded, wherefore there would be no more infinity. There is not one atom that is greater than another, else are there no atoms. But forasmuch as substance containeth the manner of all things and all things are in God, where then is the difference that is seen in the parts of this whole, between the body and the soul, between the substance and the spirit . . . between good and evil?

    [The wings of the Devil increase; his horns lengthen.]

S. ANTHONY. We go, we go! The breath of the height draweth me up! I see the planets below me!... There is no more! . . . Is this the void?

THE DEVIL. Nay, for nothing is not!

    [They rise ever.]

S. ANTHONY. [Fainting.] Shall I journey without ceasing? Where then is the goal?

THE DEVIL. In thyself! For how far soever thou dost return into the causes of things, and from whence soever thou dost draw the beginnings thereof, yet must it ever be that thou come to the end thereof, even to a former cause, to a more ancient ordering, to a God uncreated. But shouldest thou sever Him from the creation that thereby thou mightest the better make known that creation, dost thou make Him the better known? Nay, now is He the less understood without the creation than was the creation before He was.

The music of a lute is not the air that is stirred, nor is it the trembling of the strings nor is it the sound of the notes; from all these it cometh and it causeth all these. Nor shalt thou sever the music of the lute from the strings thereof, nor from its notes, more easily than thou shalt separate the creator from the created or the finite from the infinite, or the nature from the substance. For the music is by virtue of the ordering that is in it . . . therefore is it not free. God is by reason of His own self without whom He cannot be, and thence is He not free.

S. ANTHONY. Is He not free, the Almighty? He who is the Master?

THE DEVIL. [Chuckling.] Could He bring Himself to nought? . . . Can He cause that other than Himself be God, or can He become other than God?

S. ANTHONY. Yet . . . He governeth. He doth punish. He doth reward.

THE DEVIL. This doeth He in due ordering, but of His own will hath He not made that ordering, for it is by reason of that ordering that He is. For by this alone that they are, all things bring forth other things, and these latter are known unto men as the following thereof; this deed doth give birth unto that deed whence followeth yet another deed, and thence yet another, even unto five score, nor canst thou stay any one of them.

Man who doth commit evil receiveth the chastening thereof in due time; but how knowest thou that he will not be rewarded in time to come for that he hath been punished aforetime? God is no more free that He may leave evil unpunished, than thou art free to have thought that He must punish it. Thy soul containeth God inasmuch as thy soul thinketh on God. How thinketh thy soul? Even through God! Yet the infinite cannot be otherwise than in itself. In life God liveth; in thought, of Himself, He thinketh. Forasmuch as thou art, He is

I

in thee, so soon as thou hast understanding of Him. Thou art in Him, He is thee, thou art He—and there is but One.

S. ANTHONY.   There is but One !   There is but One ! Then am I a part thereof !   I, even I, am a part of God ! My body is of the substance of all substance !   My spirit is of the essence of all spirit—my soul is wholly soul ! Immortality, boundlessness, all this I have, this I am ! I know that I am Substance, I am Thought !

> [The Devil stays, floating motionless in the air. The breath of his breast that shook S. Anthony in uneven gasps is lulled. He loosens his hands. S. Anthony clings, alone, of his own hold, to his horns.]

Now I fear no more !   I am at rest.   I am immense even as the infinite that enfoldeth me.

THE DEVIL.   It is in this infinite that all things move ! When thou didst hear but now the sound of the worlds, it was not those worlds that turned them, but rather was it in thyself that this music was.   When thou wast affrighted for the gulf, thine own self did make that gulf through the lying vision of thy spirit whereby thou didst imagine measured distance in that which hath no bounds, thou didst think to see degrees in that which hath not measure.   Even this brightness wherein thou didst rejoice, who can say unto thee that it is ?

> [The Devil's gaze hollows and spins open as it were a whirlpool. S. Anthony, lost, leans towards him and begins to descend, from stage to stage, upon the antlers of his horns.]

Who saith unto thee that they are ?   Canst thou see with eyes other than thine eyes, and if they are deceived, if thy soul be the judge of all things, and that soul be a lie, where will be the surety of that which was judged ? What wilt thou be ?   What will be ?   Throughout the sleep of life man, even as a slothful god, thinketh darkly that he dreameth.   But if it be that the awakening never come? If all this be but a mockery? How if there be but nought? Aha! thou knowest not that nothingness can be? But if it be that that which cannot be be the truth, is there any truth? Thou canst discover nought, and even couldst thou discover all, never is aught known save it be by reason of the world whereof it is and of the understanding that doth receive it. If then that world itself is not, if that understanding is not! Aha! Aha!

S. ANTHONY. [Hanging in the air, floats in front of the Devil, touching him, forehead to forehead.] But thou art . . . I touch thee!

THE DEVIL. [Opening his jowl.] Ay! I go thither. I go!

> [The Devil opens his arms and S. Anthony stretches out his. But as he does so, his hand touches his robe and strikes against his rosary. He utters a cry and falls.
> He finds himself in front of his hut, stretched out flat, on his back, motionless.
> It is night and the two eyeballs of the pig gleam in the shadow; little by little S. Anthony returns to life; he raises himself, he begins feeling the earth round him, he looks about him.]

S. ANTHONY. What is it . . . what?

> [He falls back, yawning, and looks at the ruins of the chapel, vaguely, his eyes wide open.]

Ha! My pig! I had thought him dead! . . . Wherefore? I know not! . . . My heart beateth no more! Meseemeth I am as these stones, or as an empty cistern fenced about with brambles . . . and at the bottom thereof is a great black stain.

Whence come I? Where was I?

Were I to search, were I to weary myself. But I cannot! It is beyond my strength!   [He weeps.]

I understand nought of all this!

> [The outline of the Devil reappears.]

Were I to pray? But I have already prayed so much. Rather should I labour . . . then must I light the lamp again! Nay, nay! Ah me! How weary am I! I would do some deed, I know not what. I would go some-whither, and I know not whither! I know not what I would! I know not what I think! I have not even strength to desire to wish!

[A thick fog falls; the bristles of the pig quiver.] What sadness! How cold is the night! I feel as it were damp shrouds weighing upon my soul! I have death in my belly.

[He goes and sits him down upon the bench and huddles up, his arms folded, his eyes closed; then, throwing back his head, he beats it against the wall in strong regular blows; he counts them.]

One, two, three . . . one, two . . . one, two!

[He stops; the pig gets up and goes and lies down in another place.]

Whence cometh it that I do that I do, that I am that I am? I could have been other than I am; had I been born another man, then had I had another life, and I had known nought of mine own life! Were I a tree, I should bear fruit. I should be clothed with leaves, birds would perch upon me, I should be green!

Wherefore is not the pig I? Wherefore am I not the pig? Ah me! How do I suffer! I abhor mine own self! I would strangle myself could I do so!

THE PIG. I, too, am utterly weary! Rather would I be cleft into hams and hung by the houghs to the hooks of the fleshers!

[The pig flings himself down upon his belly and buries his groin in the sand. S. Anthony tears his hair, turns round, totters, stammers, and falls on the threshold of his hut.

Death appears (the pig runs away and hides). Her great shroud held by a knot on the top of her yellow skull falls to her heels and in front discovers the innermost parts of her skeleton; her cheek-bones glow, her bones clatter; in her left hand she bears a long whip whose lash trails on the ground. She is seated on a black horse, lean, great of belly, and spotted here and there where his coat is torn in patches. His worn hoofs curve back like moon-crescents; his mane, full of dry leaves, waves, and in his wide nostrils is the awful sound of the wind diving deep into caverns. When Death dismounts, he wanders away to graze among the ruins of the chapel; he stumbles among the stones and breaks them here and there. Death drops her chin on her left shoulder and shoots out the black ray of her eyeless orbits; she stretches forth her long lean hand to S. Anthony, who shudders.]

DEATH. Come! I, even I, am the consoler!

[S. Anthony half rises and stretches both arms towards Death, when suddenly appears Lust behind her, wearing a crown of roses on her head. He sits down again.]

LUST. Wherefore die, O Anthony?

DEATH. [Resuming.] Nay! Die! The world is loathly! Must thou not needs rise every morning, must thou not eat, drink, come, and go? Each one of these poor happenings is added to those that follow upon it even as thread is added to thread, and life from the one end thereof even to the other is but the endless woof of all these miseries!

S. ANTHONY. Ay, so is it! Better were it, peradventure . . .

LUST. Nay, nay!

[She takes off her crown and passes it softly under his nostrils.]

The world is fair! There be flowers whose stature is greater than thine. There be lands where the incense doth smoke toward the sun, where the voice of the turtle is heard deep in the woods, where wings beat in the blue firmament. In the summer nights the long waves of hot seas unroll their fires in the white foam, and the sky is starred with gold even as the robe of a king's daughter. Hast thou swayed upon the great weeds? Hast thou gone down into the emerald mines? Hath thy body been anointed with cool ointments? Hast thou slept upon swansdown? . . . Taste thou of this, of the life magnifical that is blessed in all his days even as the wheat hath flour in every grain of his ear. Breathe the breath of the winds, sit thee down under the citron trees; lie upon the moss, bathe in the fountains; drink wine, eat flesh; have thy desire of women; hold Nature through Nature to thee with every lust of thy being, and roll thee, even as a lover, upon her broad bosom.

       [S. Anthony sighs; she continues:] Never hast thou known in thy flesh as it were the pride of a god roaring; nor hast thou known the infinite whelm thee in the ravishment of a kiss.

THE PIG. [Howling suddenly.] I desire women mad with rutting! I long for fat middens, for mire up to mine ears! I am weary. I will flee away. I will run swiftly over the dry leaves, with the wild boars and the bears!

S. ANTHONY. Ah me! My heart melteth for the imagination of such blessedness.

DEATH. Taste of them, and thou shalt see the terror of my countenance at the bottom of the empty cup, nor shall it depart from thee.

Is not thy soul filled with fumes of retching that rise even as the smoke of a burning mountain? The wind rolleth them away and they are no more. Nor shall thy despairing abide. The sun on his way drieth the tears upon thy face. Thy determinations, thy covetings, thy godliness, thy weariness, all these shall be unravelled against the ground even as the hem of my winding sheet. Therewith I cover all mankind! Therewith do I hinder all their movements! My dry bones do

crack in their arms as they hold their love, and the last
end of their joy is that they desire to die thereof.

[But Lust leans her smiling face upon the shoulder
of Death, and the thread of her necklace is broken
thereon, and the big pearls are torn off and they
slip down, one by one, into the folds of her shroud.
Lust says :]

LUST. What matter! I make the flowers to grow
upon the tombs; all things are whirled about within
my love even as the motes of dust in the sunlight!

[S. Anthony quivers; she draws nearer to him and
touches him upon the shoulder lightly.]

Seest thou yonder little pathway in the sand? It shall
lead thee even to the gates of the cities that are full of
women. I will give thee the fairest of them, even a
virgin—thou shalt corrupt her and she shall worship thee
even as a god, in the amazement of her conquered flesh.
Haste thee! Make speed! Lo! Her raiment is cast
aside, she is stretched out among the scarlet cushions,
she lifteth up her naked arms; she would embrace thee
to her heart.

DEATH. Look thou more closely, to the foot of the
hill, see yonder great spurge? Break the boughs of it
and taste thy fingers! Then shalt thou be stretched out
to thy full length . . . thou shalt know nothing more . . .
thou shalt no more be anything!

S. ANTHONY. [Motionless, pallid, his teeth chattering.] Which shall I follow?

I have as it were a need to spew forth my life . . . yet
do I pant for desire unconstrained. Thine heat, O
Lust, that cometh forth from thy bosom enflameth my
cheek; and thy breath, O Death, chilleth the hairs of
my head.

[Death and Lust pace up and down in front of S.
Anthony in ordered movement like chanters in a
church; this is their psalm :]

LUST. My mighty voice it is that maketh the murmur

of great cities; the beating of my heart is but the throbbing of mankind.

DEATH.   The unending chain of all things maketh the whirlwind of nothingness and all the sound of the world is but the clapping together of my teeth.

SINGETH LOVEWORDS.

LUST.   I make madness to stand at the edge of unclean things.   I give joy unto the biting of the teeth in the flesh; an   enticement even in the midst of loathing.

DEATH.   The tears that I have drawn from the eyes of men would fill oceans, the great works that I have thrown down would make an heap higher than all worlds.

LUST. The harlot, covered with jewels of gold, fair with the desire of all men, singeth lovewords, softly and low of voice, beneath her smoking lamp.

DEATH. The pale worms in the night of the tomb fasten them on to the faces of the dead, as it were a swarm of bees that devour a fig.

LUST. Ay, and there be dead women whose arms hang loosely, their eyes are not fully closed, their black locks wind over their pale flesh : their nakedness is utterly discovered so that a man should say that it surpasseth and is deeper than all nakedness.

S. ANTHONY. Out upon you ! Ye are both horrible in mine eyes !

LUST. [Crying out.] For me men slay one another, men betray and kill one another. I, even I, do overwhelm life. I make the lions to roar and the flies to buzz ; I make the eagles to fly and the apes to leap ; the beds of men crack beneath their kisses, metals seethe, and the stars tremble ! . . . Come, come ! The sap of me shall flow within thy soul as it were a river of delight.

DEATH. [Her voice is now a caress.] Nay, I am kindly. I have unbound all slavery. I have ended all sadness ! Doth my sepulchre affright thee ? Nay, but it shall be dissolved even as thy bones ! . . . dost thou fear my dark loneliness ? Thou shalt be among the company of all things that rot away !

S. ANTHONY. Cease, cease ! Thine every word, as it were the stroke of a catapult, breaketh my pride even to the dust. The nothingness of all that life was, overwhelmeth me !

DEATH. I tremble beneath the earth and I swallow up the cities. I lay me down upon the waters and I overthrow the ships ; the breath of my winding sheet in the heavens maketh the stars to fall, and I walk behind all glory as it were a shepherd who watcheth his sheep at the pasture. Come hither ! Thou knowest me ! Thou art filled of me ! Without thee is nothingness, in the depth of thee is nothingness! Yet deeper goeth nothing-ness: it doth whirl even to endlessness! The coffin devoureth, the dust is scattered, and I, even I, shall take away the last grain that is over.

LUST. No stumbling-block is there, no will that I shall not break; seeing that action sufficeth not unto desire, I overflow into dreams. The man of God, deep in the cloister, seeth shapes of naked women pass about the pillars in the light of the moon; they stretch forth their arms unto him. The virgin in the hall sigheth for my faintness, the mariner sigheth upon the sea. I have hypocrisy that none may withstand and wrath that conquereth all things. I ravish purity. I enflame rap-ture; even in love crowned I dig gulfs wherein other love turneth about and about.

DEATH. [Approaching S. Anthony, lifts her arm haughtily, and speaks in her turn.] High on the cross He heard the clamour of the raging multitude that sank to rest afar off in the bye-ways. His forehead was bleeding, blood flowed from His side, a black raven pecked at His cheek, at the tears from His hollow eyes, and His locks shaken by the tempest scourged His face as it were a handful of thongs . . . then . . . [She breaks into laughter.] Even as I slay the young of the gazelle and the babes of women, so did I slay the Son of God!   [S. Anthony bursts into sobs.]

LUST. [Crying out suddenly.] Yet was nought lacking unto the first-born! The streams flowed around him to quench his thirst. The trees when he passed bowed them before his mouth. He breathed the unstained air of the world into his breast and he beheld God face to face; he hath lost all, his will was to lose all, for the savour of a kiss!   [S. Anthony raises his head again.]

DEATH. [Resumes.] But thou art stronger than God! He cannot constrain thee to live—the Power who ruleth the worlds must bend presently before this thy will to be free.

S. ANTHONY. [Bursting into a fit of wild laughter.] Yea, yea! What joy would that be!

LUST. Thou canst compel Him to create a soul. He must needs obey this the fancy of thy flesh, and thou canst strike thy root deep into nature! Thy children's children shall follow thee! Within thee thou bearest hundreds of years full of works!

S. ANTHONY. Nay! Enough, enough!

LUST. Nay, look upon my face and know it! Come! It is I! Thou didst call upon me through the covetings of mystical love; thou didst breathe my breath in the hot wind of the night-time; thou didst seek mine eyes in the stars; thou didst touch my dim shape when thou didst stretch forth thine arms in the empty air.

DEATH. Nay, remember all the bitterness of thy life! Yet didst thou desire me in thine appetite for God, thou didst cherish my tenderness in the torments of thy penitence! Come, come! I am rest, nothingness, the One Alone!

LUST. Come, come! I am the truth, the joy, the movement without end, the very self of life!

[Death yawns, and Lust smiles; the one clacks her teeth, the other kilts her gown.]

S. ANTHONY. [Draws back suddenly, raises his eyes, and cries out :] Nay, but if ye do both lie? If there be another life, O Death, and yet more pains behind thee? Or shall I find in thy joys, O Lust, yet another darker void, a wider despair?

Upon the faces of dying men have I seen as it were a smile of life everlasting, and such sadness have I beheld on the lips of the living, that I know not which of ye twain is the more death-like or the better . . . Nay, nay!

[He remains motionless, closing his eyes with his hands and stopping his ears. Death and Lust bow their heads.]

THE DEVIL. [Pinches his lip, then strikes his fore-

head and leaps upon S. Anthony and drags him back
to the back of the scene, crying out :] Hold ! Look !
  [Then is heard a great clamour ; on the horizon is
  seen a confusion of shapes passing, more intangible

THE OTHER KILTS HER GOWN.

than smoke ; then comes stones, skins of beasts,
fragments of metal, and pieces of wood ; then a
great tufted tree walking upright upon his roots ;
around his roughened trunk is a golden bracelet ;
to his boughs are hung rosaries and shells and
medals. The folk, their foreheads pressed to the

ground, trail along on their knees and fling kisses to him with their hands.

Death lifts her arm and strikes the great tree with her whip; he disappears.

Then pass IDOLS upon gliding sledges, idols black, white, green, violet, fashioned of wood, of silver, of copper, of stone, of marble, of straw, and of clay, of slate, and of the scales of fishes. They have big eyes and big nostrils, banners are planted in their bellies, their arms trail, their monstrous phalli rise even above their heads. The juices of meat flow through their beards, they sweat the oil of the sacrifice, and from their half-opened lips escape clouds of incense.

They stammer as though they would speak:
Ba—Ba—Ba—Bah.

DEATH. [Striking them.] Give place!

[Then arrive at one time the five idols that were before the Flood: Sawa whose face is that of a young woman, Yaguth with the face of a hare, Yank with the face of a horse, Nasr with the face of an eagle, Waad with the face of a man; they stream with sea-water and wrack-weed that has grown on their heads like hair. Death cracks her whip and they fall to the ground.

Then follows the great idol of Serandib all covered with carbuncles. In the holes of her eyes are swallows' nests; then the idol of Soumenat, four hundred hands-breadths in height, all fashioned of iron; she clung aforetime to walls of loadstone. Her exceeding great stature oversets her, she cracks and breaks of herself.

After her is a negro idol under a leafage of gold, smiling stupidly. She stands on her left leg in the posture of a man dancing, on her neck she wears a necklace of red flowers, and she blows ever the same note into a hollow reed. Then comes

the blue idol of Bactria, encrusted in shell of
pearl. . . .]

Swifter, swifter !

[Follows the idol of Tartary, a statue of a man in
green agate; in his silver hand he holds seven
featherless arrows.]

Hasten, hasten !

[Arrive the three hundred and sixty idols of
the Arabians, that answer to the days of the
year, increasing and dwindling in stature as they
go.]

Pass on, pass on !

[Then comes the idol of the children of Ganges
wrought of yellow leather, squatting on her legs, her
head shaven, her finger upraised The blows of
Death tear her to pieces and the tow flies from out
her limbs on all sides.

Shaking in his hands the long reins of gold that
restrain his sixty-three white-maned horses, seated
upon a throne of crystal beneath a pavilion of
pearls whose fringes are of sapphire, the Ganges
arrives, bearing all his gods in an ivory chariot. He
has the head of a bull and the horns of a ram, and
his clear-coloured robe is hidden under flowers of
the fig tree. The fringes of the pavilion sway against
one another, the manes of the horses toss, and the
immense two-wheeled car rocks, now to one side,
now to the other.

It is full; the gods encumber it : gods with many
heads, with many arms, with many feet, gleaming
with aureoles; they seem torpid, in eternal abstrac-
tion. Serpents twine about their bodies, and pass
between their thighs, then, rising and bending, bow
them above their heads as it were cradles of many
colours. They are seated on cows, on tigers, on
parrots, on gazelles, on thrones built in three
stages. Their elephants' trunks sway like censers,

their eyes glitter like stars, their teeth whirr like
sword-blades.

They bear in their hands wheels of fire that spin
round, on their breasts are triangles, round their
necks are death's-heads, upon their shoulders are
green palm-boughs. They pluck at harps and chant
hymns, they spit flames and breathe flowers. Plants
fall from their nostrils, jets of water spurt from their
heads.

Goddesses, crowned with tiaras, give suck to gods
who wail at their breasts that are round as worlds;
others suck the nails of their toes and enwrap
themselves in clear veils that reflect on their surface
the confused shape of the creations.

Death cracks her whip; the Ganges lets fall the
reins; the gods turn pale; they clutch one another,
they gnaw their arms, their sapphires break in
pieces, their lotus-flowers wither. A goddess who
bore three eggs in her apron breaks them upon the
ground.

They that had many heads cleave them with their
swords; they that were ringed with serpents
strangle themselves in their coils; they that drank
out of cups cast them over their shoulders. They
weep, they hide their faces in the carpets of their
seats.]

S. ANTHONY. [Steps forward, panting.] Wherefore
is this? Wherefore?

THE GODS OF THE GANGES. Thou Ganges of the
wide banks, whither goest thou that thou drawest us in
thy flood as it were blades of grass?

The elephant hath trembled upon his knees, the tortoise
hath drawn in her limbs, the serpent hath loosed the
tip of his tail that he held in his jaws.

Get thee back to thy source! Beyond the abode of the
sun, farther than the moon, behind the sea of milk, we
would drink again the drunkenness of our life ever-

lasting, to the sound of the lutes, in the arms of our beloved.

But ever thou flowest, ever thou flowest, thou Ganges of the wide banks!

A GOD. [All covered with eyes, black, mounted on an elephant that has three trunks.] Who hath made the sacrifice of the horse one hundred times that he should rob me of my dominion? Where are ye, my twin Twilights, ye who did trot upon asses? Where art thou, Fire, thou that ridest upon the blue ram with red horns? Where art thou, Dawn, of the vermilion brow; thou who didst draw back to thee the dark cloud of night, even as a dancer who goeth forward and draweth back her robe upon her knee?

I shone from on high. I lit the fields of slaughter. I quenched all pallor. But now it is finished! This great soul is without breadth and shall die as it were a gazelle that hath outrun its strength.

A GODDESS. [Standing upon a silver globe, coifed with flowers whence go forth rays, and clad in a scarf whereon are animals painted. A diamond necklace passes three times round her neck and over her wrists and is fastened to her heels. Milk spouts from her breasts that are encircled with gold circlets.]

From meadow to meadow, from world to world, from heaven to heaven have I fled. Yet am I the wealth of souls, the sap of trees, the colour of the lotus, the warm wave, the ripe corn in the ear, I am the goddess of slow smiles; I yawn in the jaws of the cow, I bathe me in the dew.

Ah me! I have plucked too many flowers; my head is bewildered. [Her veil flies off and she runs after it.] S. Anthony had put out his arm to seize it, but there appears:

A GOD. [Wholly blue, with the head of a boar, with rings in his ears, holding in his four hands a lotus, a conch, an orb, and a sceptre.] I have raised up the

drowned mountain from under the flood, I have borne
the world upon my tortoise back.

With my tusks have I ripped open the giant. I have
become a lion. I have become a dwarf. I have been a
priest, a warrior, a tiller of the earth. With the share
of a plough I have slain a monster who had a thousand
arms, I have done many hard and wondrous deeds ! The
creations passed away, but I remained, and even as the
ocean that receiveth all rivers nor is she ever the
greater, so did I drink in the centuries.

What now ? . . . all things reel . . . where am I ? Who
am I ? Must I bear my serpent's head ?

[A serpent's head grows upon him.]

Nay ! Rather the tail of the fish that did beat the waves !

[A fish's tail grows on him.]

Shall I put on the face of the solitary ?

[He changes into a solitary.]

Nay, nay ! It is the horse's mane that lacketh !

[A horse's mane grows on him.]

I will neigh ! I will raise my hoof ! Nay ! The lion !

[He becomes a lion.]

My tusks !   [Tusks spring in his mouth.]

All my shapes do turn them about in confusion and
escape, as though I should spew forth the lives that
travail in my stomach. Ages arrive. I shiver as one in
a fever.

> [S. Anthony opens his mouth to speak. But there
> comes :]

A GOD. [Greater than all these others, magnifical, clad
in glittering robes, riding upon a swan; he has four
faces with bearded chins; and in his hands he holds a
necklace whereon globes are threaded.] I am earth, I
am water, I am fire, I am air, I am knowledge, I am
understanding, I am creation, dissolution, cause, effect;
I am the invocation of books, the strength of the strong,
the purity of the pure, the holiness of the saint !

[He pauses, out of breath.]

K

I am the Good, the Excellent, the Most High, the sacrifice and the sweet odour of the burnt offering, the priest and the victim, the Protector, the Comforter, the Creator ! . . .   [He takes breath again.]
I am the rain that doeth good, the dung of the cow, the thread of the necklace, the refuge, the friend, the place where things must be ; I am the seed that faileth not, everlasting, ever renewed ! Coming forth at the ending of the golden egg, even as the fruit of the womb from its covering. . . .

    [He vanishes before he has time to finish his phrase.]
A BLACK GOD. [Who has one eye in his forehead, a lotus at his neck, and a triangle under his feet. He is sad of mien.] If thou dost multiply shapes of themselves, dost thou bring forth Being thereby ? Were I to dig the pits of the Pagada for ever, were I to raise the stairs of the tower continually, what should it profit me ? All that I have suffered, is it of none avail ? My many pangs of death, the toils of my lives, so much sweat, so many battles, so many victories ! . . .
Ah ! Thou nurse of mine who didst fear aforetime when thou sawedst in my mouth the shapes of the universe shining like unto rows of teeth, thou knowest not that at this hour my mouth is silent ; the jaws thereof send from the one to the other the void that they do bite !
In the midst of the forest the man of God who gazeth upon the sun prayeth with his whole soul ! He hath withdrawn him from the world, he is withdrawn from himself, he freeth him altogether.
His thought beareth him whither he will, he seeth so far as his wish is, he heareth all sounds, he taketh all shapes, but . . . were he peradventure to render not one thereof ? . . . were he to strip him of all ? Ay, by the might of his austere penitence, were he to end. . . .
    [In the manner of one affrighted.]
Oh !

[His car disappears, its axle clacking as that of a worn-out carriage.]

S. ANTHONY. [In melancholy.] No more! . . . howbeit they were Gods!

[But here be others who come forward, covered with long-haired skins. They blow between their fingers, their noses are blue.]

THE GODS OF THE NORTH. The sun fleeth! He runneth as though he were afraid, he closeth him as it were the wearied eye of an aged spinning woman.

We are a-cold, our bear-skins are heavy with snow, the toes of our feet pass through the holes in our shoon.

Of old we sat in our great halls where the logs flamed, nigh unto long tables heaped with quarters of meat and knives with carven handles.

It was good; we drank draughts of beer, we spake unto one another of our fights of old time. The horn cups clashed their golden circlets the one against the other, and our shouts rose, as it were iron hammers that a man should throw against the roof. The roof, even the wide roof, was grooved with the wood of lances! The hanging sword-blades gave light unto us during the night-time, and our bucklers were spread upon the walls from the rafters even unto the floor.

We ate of the liver of the whale in plates of copper that had been beaten out by giants. We played at ball with rocks; we hearkened unto the songs of the captive sorcerers who wept as they leant upon their stone harps, and only at dawn, when, on a sudden, the wind blew in the heated hall, did we betake us unto our beds.

Yet we must needs depart! Then did we weep, and then were our hearts swollen even as the sea when the tide beateth at the full.

On the waste land where the ravens peck, we found the apples whereof the Gods ate when they felt the hand of age heavy upon them; they were black with rot, they crushed in the rain. Deep in the forest, nigh unto the everlasting Beech, saw we the four Harts that turn about it and eat of its leaves. The bark of it was gnawed, and the beasts chewed the cud, glutted; they stood upright upon their feet, they pawed the earth with their hoofs. At the edge of the sea-shore, where the white blocks of ice are broken in pieces, we came upon the ship that is builded of the nails of the bodies of dead men; and lo! it was empty; then did the black cock

THE WHOLE FIRMAMENT THAT TURNED EVEN AS WE TURNED.

crow, he that abode below the earth in the halls of the Dead.

We are a-weary, we are a-cold, we stagger upon the ice. The wolf that runneth behind us shall eat up the moon. No longer have we the wide meadows wherein we stayed us for breathing-space in the battle. No longer have we the ships, gold-plated, even the long blue ships, whose prow cut the hills of ice when we sought upon the Ocean for the hidden Spirits who belled in the tempest. No longer have we the pointed skates whereon we fared around the poles, bearing with outstretched arms the whole firmament that turned even as we turned.

> [They vanish in a whirl of snow. Anthony feels little sympathy for the Gods of the North; they are too brutal, too narrow-minded.]

THE DEVIL. Ay! All their thought was to drink even as men that live freely! Here is one of more righteous life; he cometh from Persia!

> [S. Anthony sees an old man approaching, with slow steps, his eyes shut; his body is wrapped in much drapery, his white beard falls below his waist.
>
> In the air above his head floats a small figure which resembles him, but its lower parts are lost in thick plumage.]

THE OLD MAN. [Opens his eyes; the little figure stretches out its wings.] At last are the twelve thousand years accomplished! The day hath come, the great day! I thank thee, thou Ferver, thou First Soul, who livest for ever, for that thou didst let fall into mine understanding the wondrous rays of thine emerald eyes! Shalt thou not increase thy stature? And then shall we bathe together in the depths of the Word?   [He gives ear, he gazes.]
What is this? No more do I hear the falling of the black rain! The bodies that have been brought again to life do not rise from their graves!   [He calls:]
Kaimors! Meschia! Meschiane!   [Silence.]
My three sons have not come!

THE DEVIL. Nay!

ZOROASTER. [Starting.] Ah! It is thou, Ahrimanes!

THE DEVIL. Ay, it is I! The tempest hath blown upon thy fire, O Zoroaster! Thy wise men, uncoifed, warm their bare feet thereat, and spit in the cinders.

> [Death lashes out at Ferver with her whip; he flies headlong, crying out like a wounded quail.]

ZOROASTER. [Wanders away, with bowed head, and short steps, muttering.] Yet was it goodly! I had divided God into two separate parts; on one side was the Good, on the other the Evil.

THE DEVIL. Enough! Begone!

ZOROASTER. I had encircled life in an order of priesthood; all was in place, order upon order.

THE DEVIL. It is finished! Get thee back to thy cave!

ZOROASTER. I had taught the manner of tilth, the number of the pieces of the tamarind, the shape of saucers.

DEATH. Pass away, pass away!

ZOROASTER. There were prayers for the uprising and for the lying down and for the hours when sleep was not.

[Death breathes into his back, and his vesture swells out like the sail of a boat and urges him forward. He continues :]

Lead forward the dog that he may look upon the dying! Ye must rejoice when ye behold an hedgehog. In this wise is it lawful to quench a light that thou shalt make a wind with thine hand. Three times shalt thou rinse the raiment of the dead. With the left arm alone shalt thou hold the branches of the pomegranate tree. . . .

[His voice dies away in a vague stuttering of stupidity.

The sound of lowing is heard; a bull appears—a black bull, with double number of hairs on his tail; on his brow is a white triangle, and the mark of an eagle is on his back. His purple housing is torn, and he limps of his left thigh.]

APIS. Where are my priests, shod with reed-bark, they that did use to brush the hairs of my body, singing the while sacred words to a slow measure!

S. ANTHONY. [Laughing.] What folly!

THE DEVIL. Nay! It is a god who weepeth! Give thou thine ear!

x) p. 206

APIS. From the land of Libya I saw the Sphinx flee-
ing; he galloped even as a jackal. The crocodiles have
let fall to the bottom of the lakes the ear-pendants
that they held in their mouths. The shoulders of the
hawk-headed gods are whitened with the droppings of
birds, and the blue sky goeth alone under the painted
doorways of the empty temples.

Whither shall I go? I have browsed upon the land of
Egypt even to the last blade of grass. I drag myself
along the banks of the river, more and more do I suffer
for the wound that I had of Cambyses.

The daughters of the Pharaohs gave themselves unto
burial in caskets that were carven in mine image, and
Serapis opened not save to receive my body. But when
a ray of the sun had given his seed unto the heifer, men
ran and took me in my pasture. I was led in procession,
the castanets rang in the cornfields and the timbrels
rattled on the boats; from the desert and from the river
banks, from the plains and from the mountains, the people
of the land of Egypt ran toward me and bowed them
down before me. I was Osiris! I was God! I was
the Master Worker before their eyes, the Soul made
flesh, the Great All, visible unto men, peaceful, beautiful!

[He pauses, and snuffs the air.]

What now! I see red men who bring coals, who bear
knives; they fold back the sleeves of their garments!

THE DEVIL. They shall slay thee, fair Epaphus; they
shall devour thee; they shall tan thine hide; they shall
beat slaves with thy dried ham-strings.

[Apis departs, limping, and lowing mournfully.]

S. ANTHONY. [Looking at the Devil.] Well? What
now?

[The Devil is silent; but then come three couples
of gods, the one following the other, presently,
like the figures on a temple frieze. Uranus and
Terra, Saturn and Rhea, Zeus and Hera.
S. Anthony, amazed, says :]

Yet more!

THE DEVIL. Ay! ever more!

URANUS. [Crowned with waning stars, draws Terra by the hand, drops of blood fall from his limbs.]
Let us flee! I know not what hath broken the thread that bound the lives of men unto the movements of the stars. Saturn hath torn me and the face of God appeareth no more in the countenance of the sun.

TERRA. [White-haired, following Uranus.] I had forests of mystery, I had oceans that none might measure, I had mountains that no man might attain. In the black waters dwelt dangerous beasts, and the breath of the marshes upon my face moved as it were a dark veil.

I was terrible with power, men were drunk with my perfumes, my colours dazzled their eyes, I was huge! Ah! how fair was I when I rose from the bed of Chaos; my locks were wholly disordered!

Then did men grow pale for the sound of the abysses that were mine, for the voices of the beasts, for the eclipses of the moon. They rolled them upon my flowers, they clomb in among the leaves of my trees, they gathered white pearls and curved sea-shells upon the shore. I was Nature and I was God. I was the beginning and the ending, for Him was I Without End; His Heaven could not exceed the height of my mountains.

He hath grown greater, O Uranus! And even as thou didst aforetime with the Cyclopes, my sons, whom thou didst imprison within my bowels, even so man now holloweth out my stones that he may place his dreams therein and mark increase in his despair.

SATURN. [Savage of mien, bare-armed, his head half covered with his mantle, holding his curved harp in his hand.]
In my day the eyes of man were quiet even as the eyes of oxen.

His laughter was full and his sleep was heavy.

Against the wall of clay, under the thatched roof of boughs, the flesh of the pig smoked slowly before the clear fire of dry leaves, plucked when the cranes entered into the land. The pot seethed, it was full of mallow and asphodel. The helpless babe grew up by his mother's side. Free from wayfaring and without desire, the lone households abode in peace in the depths of the land; the tiller of the soil knew not that there were seas, the

HOLDING HIS CURVED HARP.

fisherman knew not of the plains; he who worshipped knew no other gods.

But when the pointed burdock flowered and the grass-hopper opened his wings in the yellow corn, then did men draw out the cakes of cheese from the storehouse; they drank dark wine, they sat them down under the ash-trees. Their hearts beat the stronger for the heat of the Dogstar, the threshold of their huts gave forth the smell of the goat, their maids winked their eyes as they passed by the bushes.

Never shall those days return; then was the life of

man bound down wholly unto the soil, it was even as the shadow of a sundial, nor was it turned away from its course about the fixed centre thereof!

I had cast down Uranus from his throne; wherefore then came Zeus? . . .

RHEA. I, even I, did deceive thee, thou God who devourest all things!

I was eaten up with sorrow for that I did continually bring forth, yet were my children given unto destruction that would not be satisfied. Yea! I laughed when I saw thee swallow the stone that was swaddled beneath its wrappings! Yet thou knewedst nothing! Thou didst devour it all!

[Death cracks her whip.]

SATURN. [Wraps himself in his cloak.] Let us return unto Erebus, let us return, O mine aged wife! The season of the delights of slaves is past, nor shall my cords of wool be undone any more.

ZEUS THE OLYMPIAN. [Holding in his hands an empty goblet. Before him stalks his eagle, torpid; the underside of its wings is red as though it were eaten of vermin; with its beak it picks up from the ground the feathers that fall from its body. Zeus looks into the bottom of his goblet.]

No more! Not even a drop!

[He leans it upon the nail of his finger, then sighs
—a long sigh—then speaks again :]

When the ambrosia faileth, then do the immortals depart.

Father of Gods, of kings, and of men, I ruled the firmament. I was lord of understanding and of the dominions of men. At the bending of mine eyebrows the sky trembled. I hurled the lightning, I gathered together the clouds!

I sat upon a throne of gold in the midst of all the gods, on the summit of Olympus; I opened mine eyes and I looked upon all things. I watched the Hours in their

courses, daughters of equal stature who, through
Pleasure and through Pain, are made long or short for
the sons of men; Apollo passed in his chariot, his curled
locks shook in the wind of the stars; the Rivers leant
them upon their elbows and poured forth the waters
from their urns; Hephæstus beat out his metals, Ceres
reaped her corn; Poseidon, troubled, did girdle the
echoing Earth with his blue mantle.

The clouds rose upwards and bore the sweet smell of
the burnt offerings even unto my nostrils. With the
chant of the hymns arose the smoke in the leaves of the
laurels and the breast of the high priest swelled to
the measure of the song, and gave forth in its fulness
the solemn chant of the people of the Hellenes. The
hot sun shone upon the frontals of my white temples
whose pillars are as a forest, and the breath of God
was about them even as it were a wind from Olympus.
The tribes were scattered round about me, yet they
were a people. All the nations of kings knew me for
their forefather, and the lords of the houses were even
as I am, at their hearth. I was worshipped under all
names, from the Beetle even to the Thunderer! I had
known many shapes, I had had many loves. I was a
bull, I was a swan, I was a shower of gold. I had
visited nature, and she drew me into the soul of her;
she set to it that she should become Godhead, yet
should not I cease from being God. . . . O Pheidias,
so beautiful didst thou fashion me that they that died ere
they had beheld me, accounted themselves accursed.
That thou mightest make me, thou didst take wondrous
material, gold and cedar and ivory and ebony, precious stones that were lost in the beauty thereof even
as the parts of some one nature are lost in the splendour
of one whole. Through my bosom breathed the breath
of Life; I held Victory upon mine hand, Thought was
in mine eyes, and from the two sides of my head fell
my locks as it were the free flowers of this the world

*) p. 206

made perfect. So great was I that the top of mine head touched the rafters of the roof. . . . Ah! thou son of Charmides, never could mankind excel thee, of a surety! Within the blue barrier of Panœnus, hast thou closed in for ever and ever mankind's greatest deed, and now is it for the gods to descend thereunto. I see gods who are pale for satisfying the sorrow of weary nations. They come from lands of sickness, they are covered with rags, they weep bitterly. I am not as they are, that I should dwell under cold skies, amid strange speech, in temples where are no images. I am bound by the feet unto the ancient land, there shall I be dried up nor shall I go out therefrom. Nay, I was not moved what time the Emperor Caius would take me. Within my pedestal the builders heard the sound of great laughter for the labouring with which they laboured.

Yet shall I not wholly go down into Tartarus; somewhat of me shall remain upon earth. Those into whom Thought entereth, they that understand the Ordinance and cherish Greatness, from whatsoever God they come, these shall ever be the sons of Zeus.

HERA. [Her crown on her head, wearing golden boots with curved tips, covered with a veil sown with silver stars, bearing a pomegranate in one hand and in the other a sceptre surmounted by a cuckoo.] Whither goest thou? Stay thy feet! What aileth thee? Another love forsooth? Thou fool who dost lose thy strength nor knowest that mortals are swollen with pride when they find every morning upon their pillows hairs from off the head of Zeus!

Yet was our life sweet in the constrained balance of our strife and our love. It was diverse and magnifical, it stood unchanging even as the earth with his moving oceans and his unmoved plains. Return, thou son of Saturn, return! We will lie down upon Ida, we will hide us within the clouds in the bosom of the roseate

YET WAS OUR LIFE SWEET

air, and with my white arms I will surround thy neck,
I will smile upon thee; I will pass my fingers through
the curls of thy beard and I will rejoice thine heart,
thou Father of the gods. Have I lost my dark locks or
my great eyes or my golden shoon? Is it not for thy
pleasure that I renew my maidenhood yearly in the
fountain Canathus? Am I no more beautiful? Peradventure he thinketh me aged?

What! No sound! I go, I come, I run about Olympus.
All are asleep. Even Echo seemeth to be dead.

[She cries out.]

Yea, yea! . . . my garlands of starflowers fall to pieces
at the feet of mine images. The hand of the Maenad
hath torn my robe in pieces, the hundred oxen of Argos
have lost their wreaths, my priestess, forgetful, doth
glut her with cooked fish even as a fishwife of the
harbours. O Holiness of Modesty, behold it is an
Harlot with painted cheeks that toucheth mine altars!

ATHENE. [She has her great helmet flanked with the
Sphinx, and her ægis of the golden scales; she is draped
in a peplos that falls even to her feet. She advances
holding her head in her hands.] I stagger! Yet have
I not danced, I have not loved, nor am I drunk with
wine. When the Muses sang, when Dionysus was
drunken, when Aphrodite gave herself over unto love
with all the gods, I the worker, I the ordainer, I alone
stood to my task; I considered laws, I prepared victory,
I pondered upon herbs and lands and the souls of men;
I went about in all places visiting the mighty men, I
was The Foreseeing, the Light Unconquered, the Power
even of great Zeus himself.

From what shore bloweth this wind that troubleth my
head? In what magician's bath hath my body been
bathed? Are they the juices of Medea or the ointments
of Circe the wanton? My heart faileth, I am about to
die.

ARES. [Very pale.] I fear, even as a slave that fleeth.

I hide me in the deep valleys. That I might run the better, I have undone my breastplate, I have drawn off my greaves, I have cast away my sword, I have let fall my spear.   [He looks at his hands.]
Have I no more blood in my veins, that mine hands be so pale? Ah! how I used to swell out my cheeks to the brazen trumpets! How I drave my thighs together upon the ribs of my warhorses, whose hindquarters were mighty! The red plumes twisted and shone in the sunlight; the kings held up their heads on high, they went forth from their tents, and the two hosts ringed them round that they might look upon them. I bethink me of Thero my nurse, of Bellona my companion, of my Salians who danced with heavy steps and smote upon their bucklers; greater is my sorrow than upon that night in my youth when Diomedes wounded me when I gat me up into Olympus that I might make plaint unto Zeus.
CERES. [Seated in a chariot driven by two swans' wings that beat the air; the chariot stops, and the torch that the goddess holds in her hand goes out.] Ay! Stay thy course! Forasmuch as Poseidon hath ceased to pursue me, forasmuch as I have passed around the whole earth. Go no further! Stay!
  [She takes from under her a napkin of cloth of gold and wipes her eyes therewith.]
Alas! Alas! Never more shall I see Persephone in all her glory at play amid the green shoots! She hath gone down unto the house of Pluto, nor shall she come out again therefrom.
Ye daughters of the Athenians, that wear golden grass-hoppers in your hair, ye that swaddle your babes in the robe worn in the Mysteries, ye who lie upon wild savory and eat garlic that shall drive away the vapour of your sweet odours—no more shall ye go forth of an evening, in the time of the harvest, by the Sacred Gate, in your ranks, with your heads bowed and your feet

bare, behind the Chariot that draweth the Basket, no more shall ye hear the lewd words of them that await you upon the bridge of the Cephisus.

POSEIDON. [Encased, as at Elis, in three robes, the one over the other. He all but falls at every step, he leans upon his trident.] What now? I cannot stretch my body out upon the shores nor may I run in the plains. They have constrained my ribs with banks, and my dolphins, even to the last one among them, are rotted away in the depths of the waters. Aforetime I entered upon the land. I made the earth to tremble, I was He that roareth, the Lord of floods, and men called upon Good Fortune whensoever they did sacrifice unto me. Monsters crowned with vipers barked without ceasing upon my sharp-pointed rocks. None could pass through the straits, all suffered shipwreck when they went round the islands.

Happy was the man who could one day draw up his galley upon the beach, stripped of her armament; then should he see once more his aged father and his mother and hang up the rudder of his wanderings to dry before the hearth of his home!

DEATH. Pass on, pass on!

HERCULES. [Streaming with sweat, panting. He lays down his club and wipes his face with his lion's skin; the jowl of it hangs over his shoulder.] Ah!

> [He stays a moment before he can speak, so breathless
> is he.]

Men say I have accomplished twelve toils! Rather have I accomplished an hundred, an hundred thousand, maybe! First of all I did strangle two great serpents that twined them around my cradle. I tamed the Bull of Crete, the Centaurs, the Ape-folk, and the Amazons. I slew Busiris, I strangled the Lion of Nemea, I cut off the heads of the Hydra. I slew Theodomus and Lacynus, Lycus the King of the Thebans, Euripides the King of Cos, Neleus the King of Pisa, Eurytus the King of

Oechalia. I brake the horn of Achelous that was a great river. I slew Geryon who had three bodies, and Cacus the son of Hephæstus.

Is this the full tale? Nay! I smote down the vulture of Prometheus, I bound Cerberus with a chain, I cleansed the stables of Augeas. I sundered the mountains of Calpe and of Abyla, I did but take hold of the tops of them even as one who draweth apart the splinters of a log with his two hands.

I have wandered in many lands. I have been in the land of India, I have gone about Gaul. I have passed over the wilderness where men thirst.

I freed the nations that were in slavery, I peopled the countries where no men dwelt; my strength waxed greater with the tale of mine years; I slew my friends when I did but sport with them, I brake benches when I sat me down thereon, I destroyed temples when I passed under their porches.

Within me was continual raging that overflowed in great bubbles, even as the new wine that maketh the bungs of the vats to leap.

I cried aloud, I ran, I rooted up trees, I troubled the rivers, the froth hissed at the corners of my lips, my stomach was sick within me, I wrestled in the loneliness, I called out aloud, if haply any should hear.

My strength doth choke me! It is my blood that constraineth me! I need warm baths, I desire frozen water to drink. I wish to sit upon cushions, to sleep in the daytime, to shave my beard. The Queen shall lie down upon my lionskin, I shall put her robe upon me, I shall spin with her distaff, I shall assort her wool; my hands shall be white even as those of a woman. I languish . . . give me . . . give me . . .

DEATH. Pass on, pass on!

[Arrives a great black catafalque on rollers, girt with torches from top to bottom. The daïs of it is starred with silver scales and supported by four pillars of the ordinance of Solomon round which is twined a golden vine; it shelters a bed of honour which is covered with a purple covering; upon the three-cornered bed-head stand palettes loaded with perfumes burning in vessels of painted pottery. On the bed can be seen the body of a man, in wax, lying flat, as a corpse. Round the bed are alternated in rows little silver filigree baskets and oval-shaped alabaster urns; in the baskets are lettuce plants, and in the urns is a rose-coloured pomade.

ENOUGH HAST THOU SLEPT!

Women follow the catafalque, disquiet of aspect; their unknotted hair falls the length of their bodies, as it were a veil: with their left hands they gather on to their bosoms the folds of their trailing robes and in their right hands they hold great bunches, of flowers or crystal phials filled with oil.

They draw near to the catafalque, and they say :]

THE WOMEN. He is fair! He is fair! Awake! Enough hast thou slept! Lift up thine head, get thee upon thy feet!

[They sit down upon the ground, in a ring.]

Ah! He is dead! He will not open his eyes! No

L

more will he put his hands on his hips and raise his right foot in the air and turn him round on his left heel. Weep ye! Mourn and cry aloud!

> [They utter great cries, then on a sudden are silent. The crackle of the torches can be heard, and the drops that the wind tears off them fall on to the waxen corpse and melt his eyes. The women rise to their feet.]

What shall we do? Shall we stroke him with our fingers? . . . let us beat the palms of his hands! . . . So . . . So . . . breathe of our flowers! These be narcissus and wind flower that we have plucked in thy gardens. Return to life! Thou makest us afraid! Lo, how stiff is he already!

Behold, his eyes flow at their edges! His knees are twisted, and the paint of his face is poured out on to the purple coverlet. Speak! We are thine! What is thy need? Wilt thou drink wine? Wouldest thou lie in our beds? Is it thy wish to eat of the cakes of honey that we bake in the ovens? They are shaped as little birds, for thy greater merriment.

Let us touch his belly? Let us kiss him over the heart! Ha! dost thou feel our fingers heavy with rings, passing over thy body, our lips that seek thy mouth, our hair that doth brush thy thighs? Thou god languishing, deaf to our prayers!

> [S. Anthony hides his face with his sleeve. The Devil pulls his arm sharply and pushes him closer to them.]

See, see how his limbs as we take hold of them remain in our hands! He is no more! He sneezeth not at the smoke of the dried herbs, he sigheth not for love in the midst of the sweet odours! . . . he is dead! . . . he is dead! . . .

S. ANTHONY. [Bending forward towards the women.] Who is this?

THE DEVIL. [Slowly.] These are the daughters of Tyre who mourn for Adonis.

[They flay their faces with their nails; they begin to cut off their hair, which they lay, the one after the other, upon the bed, and all those long locks tangled together look like serpents, fair and dark, crawling over that roseate waxen corpse that is now no more than a shapeless mass.

The women kneel down and sob.]

S. ANTHONY. [Holding his head in his hands.] What is this! . . . nay! . . . but I remember! Ah! once aforetime . . . on such a night, around a corpse that lay thus . . . the myrrh smoked upon the hill, near unto the open sepulchre; the sound of weeping brake forth under the black veils that were bowed over it; women wept and their tears fell upon his naked feet, like drops of water upon white marble. . . .

[He sinks to the ground.]

THE DEVIL. [Laughing.] Up, up! Here come others! Behold!

[The catafalque of Adonis has disappeared.

The sound is heard of castanets and cymbals; men clad in motley robes and followed by a crowd of peasants lead forward an ass on whose head is a plume of boughs; his tail is adorned with ribbons, his hoofs are painted, he has a frontal of plates of gold, he has shells on his ears, on his back is a casket covered with a corded cloth; it lies between two baskets, the one of which receives the offerings of the crowd as the ass moves on; eggs, grapes, soft cheeses, hares whose ears protrude, plucked fowls, pears in quantity, copper money—the other is half full, and contains rose leaves that the leaders of the ass throw before them as they walk. They have laced boots, plaited hair, great cloaks, and ear-pendants, and their cheeks are covered with paint. They wear crowns of olive branches fastened together in the middle of their foreheads by medallions whereon are tiny figures: each medallion is

set between two smaller medallions. On their bare
breasts they wear yet another larger medallion.
In their belts are bodkins and daggers, and they
brandish whips with yellow ebony handles and
triple thongs, to which are tied small sheep's bones.
First of all the men take the cloth off the casket,
that is covered underneath with black felt; the
crowd draws apart from them, the ass stops. One
of the men kilts up his gown and begins to dance
round and round, playing the castanets the while;
another kneels down before the casket and beats
a timbrel; the eldest of the band commences in
nasal tones.]

THE HIGH PRIEST. Behold the Kindly Goddess! *Cybel*
The Idæan of the mountains! The Mighty Mother of
Syria! Approach, ye worthies! She is seated between
twain lions, upon her head she beareth a crown of
towers, much good bringeth she to all who look upon
her.

We, even we, do lead her throughout the land, beneath
the fires of the sun, through the winter rains, under
fair skies and under foul skies. She climbeth the passes,
she glideth over the lawns, she crosseth the brooks.
Ofttimes for lack of lodging we sleep under the open
sky, nor is our table well spread every day. There be
robbers that dwell in the woods, the wild beasts roar
dreadfully in their caverns, there be roads that none can
pass, for the many precipices! Behold her, behold her!

[They take off the woollen covering and reveal a
casket of sycamore wood encrusted with little
pebbles.]

She is taller than the cedars, she soareth in the blue
firmament; she is more immense than the wind, she
encompasseth the world. Her breath goeth out through
the nostrils of panthers, through the leaves of plants,
through the sweat of bodies. Her tears are of silver,
they water the fields; her smile is the light, it is the

א) p. ר o ז

milk of her breast that hath whitened the moon. She maketh the fountains to flow, she causeth the beard to sprout, she cracketh the bark of the fir trees that sway in the wind. Give unto her, for she abhorreth the miserly!

[The lid of the casket is raised and reveals under a housing of red silk a little image of Cybele all a-sparkle with spangles, in a chariot of wine-coloured stone drawn by two lions with frizzly manes; their paws are uplifted. The peasants push one another to see the better, the dancing man whirls ever round and round, he who beats his timbrel beats the harder; the High Priest continues :]

Her temple is builded upon the gulf wherein the waters of the Flood were hurled when it was ended. It hath gates of gold and a ceiling of gold, canopies of gold and statues of gold. There is Apollo; Hermes is there, and the Deliveress, Atlas, Helen, Hecuba, Paris, Achilles, and Alexander. In her court walk eagles and lions, horses and doves. To her great tree that burneth men hang coats and caskets; and for her is raised the mighty phallus, whose height is one hundred and twenty cubits, whereon men climb with cords, as it were, up the trunk of a palm-tree when they go up it to pluck the dates thereof.

[They give themselves mighty blows with their whips on their backs, in measured cadence.]

Smite upon the timbrel! Clash the cymbals! Blow into the flutes that have great holes!

She loveth the black pepper that ye seek in the wilderness. She loveth the flower of the almond tree, she loveth the pomegranate and the green figs, she loveth red lips and wanton looks, sweet sap and salt tears! . . .

Blood! For thee! For thee!

Mother of the mountains, we praise thee!

[They carve their arms with daggers, their backs ring like hollow boxes. The music redoubles, the crowd grows. Then men in women's clothes and women in men's clothes pursue one another, uttering great clamour that loses itself on the horizon in the quiver of the lyres and the rustle of the kisses. Their diaphanous robes cling to their bodies. Therefrom drips roseate blood, and soon, over all that multitude of shifting tints, wavering, far-distant, appears a new god who bears between his thighs an almond-tree loaded with fruit. The veils on their heads fly off, the incense whirls, the steel rings. Eunuch priests enwrap the women in their lace-covered dalmatics.

But other gods arrive, beyond numbering, infinite. They pass like followings of dry leaves before an autumn wind, so swiftly that none can see them, and they weep, all, so loud that none can hear what they say. Death reties a knot in the lash of her whip. S. Anthony, bewildered, wishes to fly, but the Devil restrains him and resumes :]

THE DEVIL. Yonder is Atys of Phrygia. He casteth away his stone axe, he goeth to weep in the woods for his lost manhood. Here is that Derceto of Babylon who hath the hinderparts of a fish. Yonder is the ancient Oannes, there is the Deliveress covered in her veils, here is Moloch who spitteth fire through his nostrils, whose belly is filled with men, and he howleth even as a burning forest.

DEATH. [Laughing.] Aha! Behold! So hot is he in his flames that he himself melteth.

THE DEVIL. Look thou! Here be the Maidens Avengers to whom men sacrificed sucking-pigs!

THE PIG. Horror!

THE DEVIL. Yonder is the Saviour of Cities, from Elis! There be the Pure Ones of Pallantium! Yonder is Hephæstus, the Lord of smiths! Here cometh the kindly god Hermes with his hat for the rain and his shoon for the wayfaring.

DEATH. [Striking them.] Journey on! Journey on!
THE DEVIL. Here cometh the great Artemis, black,
anointed with myrrh; her elbows are pressed against
her body, her hands are opened, her feet are joined
together, lions are upon her shoulders and harts about
her womb, on her flanks are bees, she hath a necklace
of marigolds, she hath a buckler of griffins and three
ranks of breasts that shake with a great noise. But

THE MISTRESS OF HARBOURS WHO IS COIFED WITH CRAYFISH.

the skin of her body eateth her up beneath the bandages
that constrain her.   [Death laughs.]
THE DEVIL. Behold the Forager of the Patraeans,
and the Chantress of Orchomenos, the Firebearer of
the mount Crathis, Stymphalia who hath the thighs of
a bird, Eurynome the daughter of Ocean; and here be
all others called Artemis, the Midwife, the Huntress,
the Healer, the Lightbearer, the Mistress of harbours
who is coifed with crayfish.
S. ANTHONY. What is that to me? Wherefore
stayest thou me here to gape at the sight of them?

THE DEVIL. [Continuing.] She who hath white scabs on her face is Rubigo, the goddess of the itch; hard by her is Angeronia who freeth from disquiet, and the foul Perfica who discovered the staff of lust. Here is Æsculapius, the son of the Sun, drawn by his mules; his elbow is upon the rim of his chariot and his chin resteth within his left hand. It is as though he pondered deeply.

DEATH. [Striking him.] Make thyself to live, thou that diest not!

THE DEVIL. The wide-mouthed Fauns follow old Pan of the shepherds who striketh his hands together in the midst of his flock. They grin, they are hairy, their foreheads are covered with red spots even as the lime-trees in the springtime. Lo! Yonder is Priapus and the Lord of Landmarks, the goddess Epona, and Acca Laurentia, and Anna of the years that pass.

S. ANTHONY. Enough, enough! Leave me! My head is bewildered in the whirl of all these gods that pass!

THE DEVIL. Behold one who watcheth over children when they walk abroad, another who giveth fever, another who maketh men pale, another who giveth fear. These do shape the babe within the womb, those turn it round, others draw it forth, others watch over the cooking-pots, others cause the door hinges to creak, others drive the waves on to the shore.

S. ANTHONY. [Slowly.] What a multitude!

THE DEVIL. Ay, a multitude; and thou hast not seen all. And there be yet others, of whom not so much as the very dust of them can be any more found.

Yet shall they appear again upon a day, even as the dead that rise again, and man, pitiless man, shall judge them; the great and the lowly, they that were austere and they that were merry, they that had heads of beasts and they that had wings; they shall stand

*) p. 208

every one of them before him in long ranks, pale and
silent even as a conquered host. Then shall the negro
grind his teeth and draw nigh unto his idol; he shall
thrust his fist under the jaw thereof and shall spit in its
face.

The children of Javan shall overturn their white statues
with the tips of their toes in scorn, and they that dwell
in the North, whose eyes are red with the snow, shall
see their dim gods of mist and sorrow melt in the sunlight. Their bracelets and their crowns, their dried-up
urns and their rusted blades shall be cast into the winds;
the hollow of their breasts shall ring to the touch of the
finger, and the dwellers in Olympus shall crumble to
dust in the thunder of the laughter of the vengeance of
the sons of men. For they gave nought, they were
hard as the stones of their temples, and more brutish
than the beeves of their sacrifice.

S. ANTHONY. Infinite sadness is upon me!

[He weeps.]

How many prayers have men made unto them! How
many burnt offerings have smoked for them! Yet
they were strong, nor did any doubt arise touching
their majesty.

Where are ye now, ye poor souls athirst with hopes
that never were satisfied?   [He bursts into sobbing.]
What are these sounds? . . . who singeth thus?

[He listens.]

It doth crackle and buzz and twitter, and yet is there
somewhat more . . . it seemeth slow; it is unrolled,
then returneth it again!

APOLLO. [His cloak thrown back over his left arm,
he plays upon a huge lute that is held by a strap that
passes around his neck.] I sing to the lute . . .

[He coughs.]

I sing to the lute. . . . I sing of the ordering of the
world.   [He coughs.]

To the law of measure, to substance, to all that liveth.

[A string breaks and lashes his face. He tightens a pin and it breaks. He touches another and makes a mistake, he goes from one string to another; they all break with a crack and bring confusion.]

DEATH. So long hast thou been naked, so hast thou fared over all Greece, that thou canst no more, thou canst but spit, thou must die. Thou wert forsooth the purifier, the sweet singer of songs, the founder of cities? Was it not so? Now is there no song to sing, there is no city to found. The cities are all built, the fold are aged. The Prophetess is lost, nor shall she be found again.

The strong men that rubbed them with oil, the young men that ran races, the drivers who cried aloud, they stood up in their chariots of ivory, the wise men who held converse under the boughs of the rose-laurels,— *)

[She strikes him.]

Follow thou them! Begone! Fair god of the world of shapeliness that should have no end!

[Apollo slings his lute over his back and departs. Comes Bacchus, drawn by panthers. He is coifed with myrtle, and he looks at himself, smiling, in a crystal mirror. Around him are the Sileni in red woollen cloaks, the Satyrs covered with goatskins, the Maenads with their leopard skins on their shoulders; they sing, they drink, they dance, they blow on flutes, they throw on to the ground flat timbrels that spin and drone.

The Bacchantes, dishevelled, hold black masks in their hands; to the sound of the music they swing the bunches of grapes that droop over their foreheads, they devour the necklaces of dried figs that hang round their necks, they clash their bucklers together, they strike themselves with ivy-wreathed staves, they cast fierce glances about them from under eyebrows black and velvety as a caterpillar's back.

*) p. 208

The Satyrs clasp them tight in their arms; from on high they pour out the wine from their urns and smear the laughing faces of the drunken Maenads.]

THE BACCHANTS AND THE BACCHANTES. Beat down the vine poles! Trample the grape in the wine presses with your heels! Thou fair god who wearest the golden baldrick, drink thou long draughts in thy bottomless bowl! Evoé! Bacchus! Evoé!

Thou hast conquered India, Thracia, and Lydia. The hosts fled when Mimallon raged and shouted upon the mountains. The people awoke and crowded around thee. The eyes of the Bacchantes shone among the leaves. Evoé! Bacchus! Evoé!

Thou father of masques and of wine, the gods of old time stopped their ears at the wondrous offence of thy disordered measure. Thine is the new song, and thine are the measures that follow in ceaseless ordinance! Thine is the laughter of the harvesters of the vintage, thine are the hidden springs and the torchlit feasts, thine is the fox who goeth stealthily into the vines that he may eat the green grapes.

The joy of thee passeth from people to people! Thou deliverest the slave, thou art holy, thou art God, Evoé!

[Death lashes out with her whip; all disappears; then:]

THE MUSES. [Garbed in black mantles, their heads bowed.] Somewhat that is no more lived in the air when the folk were young. Their breasts were four-square and their speech fell, even as their dress, in great straight folds, fringed with gold. In the lessons of the wise teachers as in the play of the jugglers or the ordinance of the state, in the statues, in the plenishing of the house, in the trappings of horses, in the tiring of hair, in all things was fulness of beauty that uplifted life. The men of subtle thought did teach the fair women; the sculptors found mountains of marble awaiting them.

*) p. 208

S. ANTHONY. [Sighs.] Ah! It was fair! It was lovely! It was beautiful! I know it!

THE MUSES. Weep for the great theatres and the naked dancers! Thou, Thalia, thou goddess of the domed brow, where is thy brazen club, where is thy laugh that rolled upon the multitudes even as the wind of the South upon the tides that flow among the islands? Thou, grave Melpomene, thou hast lost thy quires! Forgotten is the high boot, forgotten are the trailing cloaks, forgotten is the chant that passed in gusts through the terrors of tragedy, and the strait saying that did freeze the skin! Thou, slender Terpsichore, whose daughters are the Sirens, hast thou no memory of thy measured steps that men likened unto the dancing of the stars, the while the master of the instruments did beat out the measure with his iron sole! These great raptures be ended! Now come the fighters, the hunchbacks, the jesters!

Clio hath been ravished, she hath been the servant of them that confound the governance of the city, she that was the Priestess of the great feasts groweth fat on the meats of the multitude; men have made books nor do they take thought for the speech thereof! For those whose lives are nought need frail buildings, for the service of slaves must be strait garb. The merchants and the base fellows and the harlots have bought all Beauty with the gold of their commerce; the halls of the cunning artificers are filled with all the whoredoms of the understanding, they are opened unto the multitude, they bow them to their desire; they make pleasant sport for the common folk.

Thou Shapen Beauty of ancient days, thou whose leaves were young alway, thou who didst draw in thy sap from the innermost parts of the earth, and sway thy pointed peak in the blue heaven; thy bark was rough, and thy boughs were many, and the shade of thee was spread out afar; thou didst stay the thirst of the chosen peoples with ruddy fruit that the mighty plucked. Now have the cockchafers dropped down upon thy leaves as it were a cloud; men have cleft thee in pieces, they have sawed thee into planks, they have ground thee to powder; and the asses browse upon the remnant of thy verdure.

[The Muses depart and Aphrodite arrives; she is wholly naked; she glances from side to side, disquieted. She utters a cry of terror as she perceives Lust.]

APHRODITE. Have mercy! Begone! Leave me! Thy kisses have turned my fairest colours pale! Aforetime was I free, I was pure, the seas shook for love at the touch of my heels! I bathed and none could grasp me! I swam in the blue firmament wherein my girdle, for which the west winds strove, shone, wide and magnifical, even as the rainbow fallen from Olympus. I was Beauty! I was Shapeliness! I trembled above the world asleep; Substance was dried up at the sight of mine eyes, of itself it strengthened into just shapes. The craftsman in his anguish called upon me at his task, the young man summoned me in the hour of his desire; women spake my name in the dream of their motherhood. Thou, thou, foul craving, thou hast brought dishonour upon me!

DEATH. Pass on, fair Aphrodite! Thou shalt find purity in mine arms!

[The sound is heard of one sobbing.]

EROS. [Appears, blear-eyed, lean, puny, gasping, wretched. His fillet is too loose, it has fallen over his face; he weeps noisily, he digs his fist into his eye.]
Is it my fault? [He weeps.]
Aforetime all the world did cherish me.

[Again he weeps.]

My torch is quenched!
I have lost mine arrows; once was I cradled in green gardens. My finger was upon my lips, I smiled, my

locks were curled, ever I moved in loveliness. I was wreathed with roses, I was garlanded in riddles and cunning speech. I made sport unto myself in Olympus with the ensigns of the gods. I was the enchantment of life, the lord of souls, trouble everlasting.

I shiver for hunger, for cold, for weariness, and for sorrow. Now are all hearts won by Mammon. When I knock at the doors of men, they make pretence to be deaf! Some have I seen who looked upon me with a fierce eye, who betook them again to their work.

DEATH. Away with thee! Begone! The world is weary of thy name! Thou hast set its teeth on edge with the honey of thy fondness! [She kicks him.]

THE GODS OF THE HEARTH. [Covered with worn-out skins of dogs, squatting, their knees against their chins, like old mangy apes.] We . . .

DEATH. [Striking them.] Pass on, pass on!

THE GODS OF THE HEARTH. The house is open, the keys are lost, the host hath betrayed his faith! No more are men-servants submiss, children do no more honour their parents, no more are fathers feared, no longer are there great families! . In the ashes the cricket mourneth for the dead remembrance, for the worship of the home!

> [Death wipes her brow with the skirt of her
> shroud; S. Anthony stands motionless with his
> eyes fixed on the horizon; yonder comes the
> dwarf-god Crepitus, rolling in mid air, bluish,
> lightfloating.]

CREPITUS. [In a fluty voice.] I too was honoured aforetime. Men poured forth wine before me. I was a god.

The Athenian hailed me as an herald of good fortune; the godly Roman cursed me and clenched his fists; the priest of Egypt abstained from eating of beans, he trembled at my voice, he grew pale at the smell of me. When the vinegar of the soldiers flowed over the

*) p. 208

**) p. 209

untrimmed beards, while men feasted on acorns and shallots and raw onions, while the torn goat's flesh seethed in the sour butter of the shepherds, then no man gave heed to his neighbour, none were constrained. The solid food gave strength of sound unto the stomach—in the sunlight of the fields men eased them slowly.

So went I without offence, even as the other needs of daily life, even as Mena who tormenteth the virgins, or gentle Rumina who watched over the breast of the nurse that is swollen with blue veins. I was merry, I called forth laughter! The guests lay at ease by reason of me and breathed forth their merriment through the openings of their bodies.

I have known days of pride! The good Aristophanes sent me forth in the Masque, the emperor Claudius made me sit at his table. In the folds of the dress of the nobles I went about in majesty. The vessels of gold sounded beneath me, even as dulcimers, and when the bowels of the master, filled with lampreys, with truffles, and with pasties, disgorged them noisily, the watchful world learnt that Cæsar had dined.

But now men are red with shame for me. They strive to hide me. Only among the common folk am I known; men cry aloud at my name!

       [Crepitus vanishes with a moan.]
  [Silence. A clap of thunder! The Devil trembles.
  S. Anthony falls, face downwards, to the earth.]

A VOICE. I was the Lord of hosts! I was the Lord, the Lord God!

I was terrible as the jaws of a lion, I was mightier than the torrents. I was higher than the mountains. I appeared in the clouds with a wrathful countenance.

I led the fathers of the people who went in search of wives who should bear seed unto them. I governed the steps of the swift dromedaries, I appointed the meeting-places at the edge of the well whereon was the shadow of a yellow palm-tree.

I let loose the rain as it were through taps of silver, I sundered the seas with my feet, I clapped the cedars together with mine hands; upon the hills I unfolded the tents of Jacob, I led my people in their flight across the sands.

I, even I, burnt Sodom. I, even I, drowned the whole earth in the flood. I swallowed up Pharaoh with his princes the sons of kings, with their chariots of war and their drivers.

I was a jealous god, I hated the other gods, I abhorred the other peoples, and my chosen people I chastened with pitiless wrath. I brayed the unclean to powder as in a mortar, I cast down the proud; my desolation went forth to the right and to the left even as a camel that is let loose in a field of corn.

I chose out the simple to deliver Israel. Angels with wings of flame spake unto them in the bushes; then did the shepherds cast down their staves, they went forth to war. The women anointed themselves with spikenard and cinnamon and myrrh; they put on fine raiment, and shoon with high heels, they went, full of good courage and brave of heart; they sought out the captains, they cut off their heads. Then did my glory ring forth above the sound of the cymbals. In the roll of the thunder it spake aloud upon the mountains; the wind as it passed ravished the prophets; they rolled them naked in the dry valleys; they lay flat upon their bellies that they might hearken unto the voice of the sea; they rose up suddenly and called upon my name.

They came by night into the halls of kings, upon the carpet of the throne they shook the dust from off their cloaks; they called down my vengeance; they spake of Babylon and the stripes of slavery. The lions were mild before them, the flames of the furnace drew aside from their bodies, the wizards howled aloud in their anger and cut themselves with knives.

*) p. 209

I graved my law upon tables of stone; I bound my people therewith as it were the belt of a wayfarer that constraineth his body. They were my people—I was their God! The earth was mine, all men were mine, their thoughts and their works, their tools of the field and their houses. Mine ark lay in a threefold sanctuary behind the veils of purple and the lighted candlesticks. One whole tribe did serve before me, they swung the censers; they builded me a ceiling of beams of cedar-wood— the high priest was robed in robes whose colour was as the colour of an hyacinth, he wore on his breast precious stones set in ordered rows.

Evil! Evil! The Holy of Holies is opened. The veil is rent, the ark is lost, the savour of the sacrifice hath gone out into all the winds through the rifts in the walls. In the sepulchres of Israel the vulture of Libya sheltereth her brood. My temple is destroyed, my people are scattered. They have strangled the priests with the cords of their vesture; the strong men have perished by the sword, the women are led captive; the vessels are molten, every one of them.

This is that God of Nazareth who hath passed through Judæa. Even as a whirlwind in the autumn, so hath he drawn away my servants. His apostles have churches, and his mother, also his family, and all his friends; I, even I, have not one temple! There is no prayer for me alone! Not a stone that beareth my name graven thereon! Nor is Jordan of the muddy waters more sorrowful and desolate than I am.

[The Voice passes away.]

I was the Lord of hosts! The Lord! The Lord God!
   [Death yawns. S. Anthony is stretched upon the
   ground, unmoving. Lust leans her back against the
   door of the hut, her right knee is drawn up on to her
   left knee; she unravels the hem of her gown, and the
   threads of it, swayed by the wind, flutter about the
   pig, fall upon his eyelids, and tickle his nostrils.]
M

THE DEVIL. [Stretches out his claw and lays it upon S. Anthony and cries :] They have passed away !

LOGIC. Verily, and in truth, forasmuch as they . . .

[S. Anthony opens his eyes once more.]

Forasmuch as they have passed away, thy god also . . .

S. ANTHONY. [Rises to his feet, seizes a pebble and hurls it at Logic.] Nay ! Never ! Thou art death unto the soul ! Get thee behind me !

[He kneels down.]

Pity, O my God ! Pardon me ! Love me ! . . . It is Thy grace that maketh men pure, Thy love that maketh them good. Have pity on me, have pity !

THE DEVIL. There is no pity ! Compassion shall not descend upon a sinner such as thou art.

S. ANTHONY. [Praying.] O Jesus, thou Son of God, Who art God even as the Father, God even as the Holy Spirit ! . . . Ye are One !

THE DEVIL. I am many ! My name is Legion !

S. ANTHONY. Thou didst send Thy Son . . .

THE DEVIL. Another shall come !

S. ANTHONY. To stablish Thy church !

THE DEVIL. He shall overturn it !

[The Devil, placing himself behind S. Anthony, shouts in his ear so loudly that S. Anthony on his knees bends like a reed, now falling on to his wrists, now raising himself again, yet ever continuing his prayer ; the Devil says the while :]

He shall be born in Babylon, likewise of a virgin, one made holy unto the Lord, but who shall have committed fornication with her father. He shall cause himself to be circumcised among the Hebrews ; he shall build up again the Temple. He shall convert first of all proconsuls, then princes and kings—the Emperor of Taprobane, the Queen of Scythia, and three popes, the one after the other. He shall send his messengers over all ways and his prophets unto all nations, and his armed men against all cities.

He shall be fair to look upon; women shall be driven to madness because of him.

He shall fill the multitudes with food; men shall fall asleep at the gates; their stomachs shall be filled even to their teeth. He shall satisfy the lust of the lustful, the greed of the covetous, the desire of the eye, the jealous belly. He shall raise up the mighty and shall put down the humble; he shall slay the faithful with the sword, he shall smite them to earth with clubs, he shall grind them to powder with pestles, and he shall burn every sanctuary as it were an henroost that is full of vermin.

The mules of his slaves shall lie upon litter of laurels, they shall eat up the flour of the poor in the cradle of Christ Jesus. He shall establish gladiators upon the hill of Calvary, and in the place of the Holy Sepulchre shall he set up a brothel of black women who shall wear rings in their noses and shall cry aloud words of horror.

He shall walk upon the sea, he shall fly in the air, and he shall descend beneath the earth as it were a fish that plungeth. He shall raise up tempests, he shall still the waves of the sea. He shall make the dead trees to blossom and he shall wither up the trees that are in flower. Diamonds shall flow over his sandals and sweet odours shall come forth from his breath. Wheresoever he shall bear his hands there shall flow drops of blood, and he shall make answer, " I am Messias."

S. ANTHONY. [Praying.] O Dove of the Holy Spirit, cause the coolness of the winds of heaven to pass over my face. Let my tears flow and bear away my soul into the outpouring of love without end.

THE DEVIL. He shall summon the soothsayers from all lands; he shall speak all tongues; he shall understand all writings. It shall be as though the whole world were mad, and men shall say unto one another : " What shall this be? What is this that cometh to pass? " And when he shall have preached over all the earth for the space of two years and one hundred and eighty and three days; when he shall have persecuted the faithful so that they turn them away from their faith or testify unto it in death; when he shall have overthrown the Holy Places and opened all dungeons, and slain all the priests, and gathered unto him the multitudes; when he shall possess kingdoms and treasures and armed hosts, then shall the Heavens send down at one time the prophet Elias and the prophet Enoch; and he shall slay Elias and he shall slay Enoch; their skulls shall be scratched with the points of spears; they shall be boxes for paints and caskets for sweet odours.

S. ANTHONY. I hear the voice of the evil one that howleth round about me; but in thy strength, O Lord Almighty, will I laugh his wrath to scorn. I will sing thy praises during the terror of temptation. Lo, I am even as one that falleth into the sea, who giveth great strokes with his loins that he may get him again into his boat. Take me unto thee, O Lord; receive me; show unto me thy pity and loving-kindness.

THE DEVIL. Then shall the dream of evil blossom as a flower of the darkness, greater than the sun. Then shall there be raptures of pride so bitter and so long, and delights of lust so furious, and so overwhelming a pestilence of nothing, that the angels shall rend their wings and the holy men shall curse their holiness, the martyrs shall repent them of their torment, and the chosen of God shall gather around Jesus and shall scoff at Him in their wrath. He shall be forsaken in His heaven; hell shall overflow her borders and shall be poured forth over all the earth:

[S. Anthony continues his prayer. Pride bows her head and withdraws her into her mantle. Anger stands motionless. Envy closes her eyes. All the daughters of the Evil One are in consternation. But the Devil opens his great green wing, and whirling it rapidly round and round like a sling he rubs it against the lips of the seven Sins, who rush helter-skelter round S. Anthony, howling horribly.]

LUST. Wouldest thou virgins white as the moon? Or lovest thou better women whose colour is as amber, whose mocking is haughty, who shall twine even as vipers in the coils of wantonness that findeth ever a new thing? It is more fierce than hatred, it is earnest as prayer. Thou shalt feel against thy flanks the cold of their golden bracelets, and thy flesh shall leap beneath their kisses, thy soul shall melt in their eyeballs, all thy being shall be dissolved in the vapours of raging madness.

ANGER. Hither! Hither! Thou shalt disgorge thy soul of the fury that doth stifle her; thou knowest not the delights of murder, the rapture that cometh upon thee when thou dost lift up the knife, the joy that eateth thee up when it falleth again and driveth deep.

GREED. Thou shalt have at once and for thyself alone spiced red flesh, steaming more than a cloud; thou shalt have thick frozen drink, Thou shalt eat of fruits whose colour quivereth, that seem to be alive even as the beasts. Thou shalt eat thereof and thou shalt drink thereof continually and without ceasing, even until thou dost slaver and burst in sunder.

AVARICE. Wouldest thou heaps of gold, palaces, peoples, and ships with purple sails, wouldest thou baths of jasper? Thou shalt roll thyself upon mounds of silver piled up as it were cut clover, and at the clash of the metal thou shalt hear in thy heart the sound of all corruption and all dominion.

S. ANTHONY. Nay, nay. I love better the rattle of my rosary, the wood of my crucifix, and the hard earth of my cell floor.

ENVY. All that thou couldest not attain unto, that will I abase for thy satisfying. Thou shalt see the wise men confounded, and the great brought low, and the rich made poor; the fair scornful women after whom thou hast lusted shall weep beneath the lantern of a brothel amidst shipmen and carters who shall spit in their faces.

SLOTH.   Bury thyself close in sleep, plunge thee in the blessedness of slothfulness! Thy thought, even as a vulture that hath lost his breath, shall shorten and ever shorten her flight that she may alight upon the earth. Thou shalt taste of the stillness of nothing in the delight of living, and thou shalt come to be as it were a trembling, like unto a plant made man.

SCIENCE. [Triumphing.] I will discover unto thee the place where suns shall appear, I will shew unto thee the cavern on the shores of the sea where rotteth the body of Cleopatra. I will raise up again the ages and I will open the earth before thine eyes; thou shalt understand Nature and Thought, good and evil, and thine unbounded love shall enfold all the manifold creation even as the firmament. A thirst for the truth, more faithful than is the hope of Heaven, shall compel thee toward God, and thou shalt feel Him grow in the outspreading of thine understanding like as the firmament that shall be widened even as thy thought is unfolded day by day.

PRIDE. Thou must be unto thyself as though thou wast the centre of the world; thou shalt be pure and thou shalt be strong, wholly untroubled and great of understanding even as the Lord Himself. Up! Lift up thine head! Stand face to face with God! Spurn all things! There is no triumph whereof the worth is as the joy of making mockery thereof; nay, this doth surpass even the highest mountain-tops, even this that thou shouldest spurn them for that they are too low. Tend thou this fierce pleasure for thyself, scratch upon thy sore, worship thine own self.

S. ANTHONY. I will abase myself, O Lord, I will bow my forehead and my pride in the dust. I would stand continually before Thee even as a ram upon the altar, as the kine of a smoking burnt offering.

*) p. 209

[Then the Devil waves aside all the Sins with his hand, and advances, stooping, towards S. Anthony.] Ay! drive them back! They are aged, and thou needest them no more to compel thee to me. Seest thou not what desire after evil maketh men to pant in the chase after me, since the beginning of the world? But we meet—now, even now, I hold them in my arms. The breath of my mouth is the air of their thoughts, and I who damned them through the body now damn them through the understanding. A new madness compelleth mankind into the abysm, for they are glutted. Dost thou hear the principalities and powers? They rot, they crack in the darkness even as palaces that fall to the ground? The Gods are dead and Babel is again up-lifted. Evil doth triumph at the last; and in the vastness that he hath conquered, he proclaimeth by the voices of all things his great and awful hosannah for that he hath been made God. Wouldest thou that he enter within thee? Wouldest thou feast thee upon his infinite beauty? Wouldest thou become the Devil?

S. ANTHONY. [Praying.] Pity! Pity! Blessed be Thy name, blessed be Thy works, and blessed be Thine anger! I seek not to understand Thee, I seek only to love Thee; I desire not to live, I would not die. O Holy Virgin! O Christ Jesus! O Holy Spirit! Pity! Be pitiful unto me!

[Then the sky is rent open and clouds gathering greatly upon themselves reveal the sun who appears in the midst of them—an immense sun, gold-coloured, with great slanting rays that pass between the swellings of the clouds like the ropes of a pavilion half opened. The sun strikes full on S. Anthony's face. The Devil bows his head; the Sins, livid and all a-sweat, rattle in the throat from exhaustion.]

THE PIG. [Rejoicing.] Ah! the good sun! Such fear had I in the night!

THE DEVIL. [In a strong voice.] The hour hath struck! We must go hence!

[Death mounts her steed once more; the Sins have disappeared.]

S. ANTHONY. [Raises his arms to heaven; the tears flow from his eyes; he cries out:] I thank Thee, I give thanks unto Thee, O Lord!

THE DEVIL. [Turns in one bound and says to him:] What matter! Seeing that the sins are in thine heart, and that desolation rolleth about within thine head! Draw thy shirt of hair close about thee, fast, tear thyself in pieces, humble thee. Search thou for sayings of highest holiness, seek out the bitterest penitence, and then shalt thou feel vapours of wantonness that flow within thy wounded flesh. Thine empty stomach shall call for the great feasts, and the words of thy prayer shall be changed in thy mouth even unto cries of despair. The satisfaction of thy godliness shall swell thee with pride, the weariness of thy merit shall summon up envy unto thee! When lust after all things hath left thee, then shall come the covetings of the spirit, and thou shalt beat with thine head upon the stones of the altar, thou shalt kiss thy cross, but the flame of thine heart shall not warm the metal of it! Thou shalt search for a knife; I shall return, I shall return!

S. ANTHONY. [Praying.] As it may please Thee, O Lord! [The Devil goes away, laughing.]

S. ANTHONY. Make me to love Thee!

THE DEVIL. Ha, ha, ha!

S. ANTHONY. Jesus, sweet Jesus!

THE DEVIL. Ha, ha, ha!

S. ANTHONY. Have pity upon me, have pity upon me!

THE DEVIL. Ha, ha, ha!

S. ANTHONY. Jesus, Jesus!

THE DEVIL. Ha, ha, ha!

[The Devil's laugh repeats in the distance; S. Anthony continues his prayer.]

FRAGMENTS

FRAGMENTS

THE fragments which we give in the pages that follow this belong to the 1848 manuscript. Although they were suppressed by Flaubert in the corrected text of 1856—as were a large number of other passages—we consider it right to publish them on account of their literary value. It is evident that the best course would be to publish the first manuscript in its entirety; but that first manuscript is, after all, no more than a rough draft wherein it would be difficult to rediscover the definite scheme of the author through all his numerous variants. Besides, it does not seem to us that the moment has yet come for presenting that vast preliminary study to the public.

When we published the 1856 manuscript—*i.e.* the version the reader has just perused—in the "Revue de Paris," it seemed well to intercalate these fragments in our text so as not to weary the attention of the reader by perpetual references to the foot of the page, and, above all, so as to avoid injuring the literary effect. Our procedure was in no way arbitrary; all we did was to re-establish these fragments, which had been suppressed by the author, in the places which they occupied in the 1849 draft.

[Note by M. L. Bertrand.]

I

(Pp. 31 etc. of MS.)

LUST.   Great saints there be who are wedded!

LOGIC.   In very deed, doth virginity of the body suffice that a man shall achieve his salvation?

LUST.   Moreover, he can keep his continence; he maketh oath and thereby is he bound! But at the least thou wouldest have a mate who should avail more than a friend and be more tender than a mother to soothe thy sorrow!... Adam, what day his banishment was begun, was nigh unto being comforted that same eventide when he felt upon his forehead the lips of Eve that were pressed thereto. She stroked his face, and they beheld in one another's eyes visions as fair as those of the land of blessedness that they had lost . . . Ah! didst thou know how women can tend suffering, how their smile can melt away even the most icy bitterness! Because of them are born the sorrows of life, whether it be that they draw these unto them or that they drive them away. And, from the very bent of its path, ever the heart of man shall go forth, pouring itself into their tenderness . . .

ANGER.   Thou shouldest have ridden upon an horse, thine helmet upon thine head, thy long sword beating against thy bare leg, or else thou shouldest have borne upon thy back the iron-shod stakes, and sung with thy stout comrades in the ranks. . . . Thou wouldest have marched upon the great highways of the world and passed through the dark forests; thou wouldest have pitched upon the heath and drunk of the waters of strange lands; thou wouldest have besieged the strong

172

castles and beaten down the great gates of the chief
cities; with the stave of thy spear wouldest thou have
broken up the painted pavements of palaces. . . .

LUST. Ay, and drawn their fair women by the hair. . . .

PRIDE. How beautiful is he, the conqueror, when
he entereth into the cities, to the sound of the brass
instruments, when the people go up on to the housetops
that they may see his face!

S. ANTHONY. Nay, I was too weak to wear the
breastplate!

LOGIC. Yet canst thou wear the hair-shirt!

PRIDE. Had not the pride of thy godliness cast thee,
when thou wast yet a child, into the ignorance that
shutteth thee in, thou wouldest be a wise man and
a doctor; thou couldest have sat at the feet of the
pillars and unrolled upon thy knee the writings of the
learned men; thou wouldest have followed with thy
finger the course of the kingdoms and the path of the
planets in the heavens! Thy life would have run its
course softly, even as thou didst read, itself like unto a
book, and its days should have fled more swiftly than
the words thereof, nor shouldest thou be disquieted one
whit for the great number of the pages that remained
for thee to turn.

Ay, and in knowledge are there mad spasms and enchant-
ments without end. Never hath man dried up her
dugs ever since the sons of men have pulled thereat.
At her kiss of love a great light would have flamed within
thine head; yea, the imagination of thine head would
have moved upon the waters even as a torch: the beam
of it would have been spread out in the depths thereof
as in a mirror, and the crests of its light would have
been multiplied even to thousand thousands. The
world would have passed on, below thee, bewildered
in the shadow, without sound.

II

(Pp. 269 etc.)

THE WOMAN WITH THE DAGGER. [She comes up and smiles in the very face of S. Anthony; she turns her head on one side and shows her teeth, rolling her eyes.] I am Adultery! Man tempereth his heart in my breath; ever I hover in his sleep, as it were a butterfly shut in the net that is about the bed. From the one end of the world even unto the other end thereof I draw the bodies that must come together. Betwixt their wills glideth my fancy, and even in love crowned I dig gulfs, wherein other love is whirled about and about! . . .

Have they told thee their dreams, the thoughtful young men? The bride riseth up, bare-footed; she walketh warily down the dark corridor. Her raiment is wet with the damp of her body; as she passeth, it fanneth the flame of the flickering rushlight. She smileth, she layeth her finger upon her lips, she sheweth that she feareth the babe that turneth him in his cradle.

My delight is the sweetness of betrayal that none know of! Mine are the bodies that are twined together in rapture, the long kisses under the moon, the swift flights across fields, where they gallop madly; the wind is in their cloaks; they cease not to clasp one another. Mine is also the madness that draweth crime; mine are the philtres, and the self-slayings, and the craven poisons that are poured forth by soft hands! . . .

THE WOMAN WITH THE LOOSENED HEAD-BAND. [She clasps her hands and cries:] I am Fornication. The anthills are aswarm with love, the

*)see p 205, note to p. 173

I MAKE THE FLOWERS TO GROW

she-leopard whineth in the cane-trees, and the harlot, hoarse of speech, doth sing, in a low voice, foul words on the threshold of her house . . . at that hour are the lamps lit; they hang from the ceiling, they swing in the hot wind of the summer nights. Then is the vesture undone, the naked women fling them down upon the great beds! . . . Unroll my hair, thou shalt see how long it is! My stature is slender, my flank is broad. My hams are supple, they leap more truly than steel; I crackle my bones when I am bent back on my haunches. The cup of mine enchantment doth smoke at the head of my bed; enough that a man drink thereof, for then shall he never lose the taste of it. I have odours that compel love, the red genital standeth up in my hand . . . come into the holy wood; it is filled with the sweet smell of the larch-trees! We will lie down in the sun, we will roll our madness at the feet of the painted idols! . . .

THE FRIZZLED WOMAN. [Drags herself forward on her croup.] I am Foulness. I am the Goddess of unclean imaginations and the couplings of beasts. In the cities have I seen pale women who sighed for other women, and children that wept bitterly in the arms of aged men; I have seen young men who walked like maidens and smiled at the street corners. My need is the well-fastened door that I may fulfil my lusts. I love swollen tissues, organs beyond nature, monstrous minglings of sex, bitter sweat, and disgust that doth irk. Beyond all pleasures is Pleasure! . . . wide is the circle of joys unknown! Even as is the spirit, so is the flesh without end, and the sons of Eve, for so long that they have dug therein, find never the bottom thereof! . . . Hither, hither, look upon me! My teats hang down from my breast! My huge belly doth rise and fall even as a tide, I handle my flesh with both hands! . . .

III

(Pp. 292 of MS.)

THE POETS AND STROLLING PLAYERS.

Ho, hé, ho, hé !

We balance in. mid air. We wander over the roads, we hurl ourselves headlong to make sport for them that behold us, we are driven thereto, we know not why !

We swallow sharp blades, we put upon us crushing burdens, we dwell with perilous things.

Many days it needed to go into far countries and seek out wild beasts ; it needed strength to conquer them and craft—of a truth—that we might supple their leaping to the measure of the music, that we might make them roar at our will and drag themselves upon their bellies.

It may well be that not all men were born to bear pyramids of mankind upon their foreheads, to have ever at their bed-head the claws of raging beasts that scratch behind the wall !

Even as men do with a ship, whereinto they drive trenails with the blows of a mallet, and they harden the wood thereof with fire and close together the timbers with screws—even so have we driven many hard things into our souls ; we have girdled them with iron that their course may be straight in their faring, that their springing masts may fly the higher, that they may be proud beneath the sunlight as they cleave the waters with their painted hulls. Yea, we have suffered in the days of our youth, we have looked upon ourselves in mirrors that we might learn the manner of face that maketh the multitudes to weep.

We make rhymes upon wine and upon feasting, yet we drink but water; we make men to weep for love, yet we know not love. The ruddy-faced man at arms doth bawl our strange songs as he goeth into the battle. The lewd men of simple wit covet our cheerfulness. The women who have been deceived weep upon our bosoms, and ask us that they may know what we have done that we should learn to shew forth so well the love that devoureth them, even though we seem not to understand it!

Ho, hé, ho, hé!

We have crowns of painted paper, we have swords of wood, we have tinsel on our vesture. . . . The false diamonds shine more brightly than the true; the rose-coloured hosen are better than white thighs; our wigs are as long as the locks of a woman's hair, they smell as sweet when we grease them, they are as pleasant to the touch when we tire them, as fair are they with changing lights of gold and of silver when the sun passeth through them. The paint upon our cheeks sheweth forth our boldness of passion, our pads of cotton do kindle men to desire adultery; the gold braid upon our rags that flappeth in the wind as we dance at the crossways doth arouse wise thoughts upon the frailty of all things of this life.

We sing, we cry aloud, we weep, we leap upon the rope, holding our long balancing staves. The musicians make great noise, the barn trembleth thereto, the mists come and go, the colours of all things change, our thoughts swell, the crowd doth press close, we pant for breath, our eyes are fixed upon the goal, we are deep in our task; so do we fulfil the strange fancy that shall make men laugh for pity or cry aloud for terror.

We are deafened by our tumult, we are made sad by our joys and wearied for our sorrows . . . we have convulsions therefrom, and aching of the limbs, and noisome growths! . . . how long have we laboured upon the

N

earth, shewing forth ever the same tale of laughter! Apes, and parrots, strange words and ribbons, women of exceeding great stature, and high thoughts! How often have we looked upward to the stars and said again the same saying! We have shaken off the dew of the spring, we have sung the love-tale of the linnet! We have likened the leaves to vain dreams, and the sons of men to grains of sand, the young girls to roses!

We have spoken, even to weariness, of the moon and of the sun and of the sea! Nay, the moon hath grown pale, and the heat of the sun is less; nay, the very Ocean seemeth to be diminished.

We left our fathers and our mothers. We have forgotten our country, we carry our gods in the carts wherein we travel. When we pass through the land, the folk leave the plough; mothers hold their children by the hand for fear lest we take them away with us.

Men have spat upon our lutes, they have covered with mire the patterns of diamonds that are crossed upon our breasts. The rain from the gutters hath trickled down our backs, all the despair of life hath poured through our souls; we have gone into the fields that we might weep alone. . . .

Ho, hé, ho, hé!

Let us wipe off upon the grass the dust that befouleth our golden shoon, let us lift up our heads, let us be fair to look upon, and proud! Turn we, turn we, upon our trained horses who gallop without resting, who fling the sand in the faces of the people that hail us! Thought, even as they, with red knots in her mane, beareth us on her crupper whereupon we stand upright. Let us breathe in the smoke of her nostrils, let us crack our fingers, let us beat with our heels that she may run yet more swiftly . . .

Ho, hé, ho, hé! . . .

x) p. 209

IV

THE PIGMIES. [Singing before S. Anthony.] We little mannikins do swarm upon the earth even as the lice on the back of a beggar. Men may crush us or burn us with fire, they may drown us or strike us down; yet do we appear again without end, the more full of life and the greater in number, terrible for the host of us.

Wonderful is our Dominion. If luck be with thee, thou shalt surely gather much wealth therein; art thou duly disposed, thou shalt be happy. We have men of wise thought, we have men that cleanse the city by night, we have harlots, and folk that make hats, and men who search after nature. We go out and we come in. We sit down to table and we make merry. We go to bed, we quarrel, and we love one another. We have thoughts, we hold argument, we rouse us to fiery speech. Our boats, wrought of a nutshell, do cross the brook, and the mariners are pale for fright, for the tempest is terrible. The hunters in the grass give chase to fleas; beneath the tree that sheltereth us there be kingdoms overturned, nor doth it trouble the sparrow who singeth among the leaves thereof, nor the ants who crawl about the bark of it.

Seest thou our houses and our bridges, our aqueducts, our companies of armed men, our houses of Council? . . . Seest thou our schools, and the children of the Pigmies who learn therein, the teachers who discourse before them, the little books, and the little pens? Seest thou the poets of the Pigmies who sing of the kings of the Pigmies; seest thou the thieves of the Pigmies, the

scornful, and the downcast among us? Dost thou see
the Pigmy physicians who go to visit the Pigmy sick?
They feel the pulse in their wrist, they sit them down.
The sick man sheweth his tongue, the physician rolleth
his eye; he putteth on a bandage, he giveth him a pill,
then he holdeth converse with the parents; then he
riseth up and receiveth a little piece of silver, he putteth
it in his little pocket, wherewith he may buy for his
little needs. Yet the little sick man is downcast to see
his little physician depart. Cometh a little priest,
and the little sick man dieth; the little physician
eateth his dinner. Then do they make a little coffin,
they shed their little tears; they have their little pomp
and ceremony of followers, and they seek out a little
corner of ground wherein they may lay the little corpse
that shall rot to carrion! . . .

V

(Pp. 398 etc. MS.)

[Death draws near to S. Anthony. She gazes into his face, without moving; her arms hang down by her side, her wrists are crossed. She lowers her head upon the tendons of her neck, twists her mouth awry and smiles. S. Anthony shudders.]

DEATH. If thou art cold, thou shalt no more be cold.
Art thou hungry?—thou shalt feel no more hunger.
Art thou sorrowful?—thou shalt know no more sorrow!

[She takes a step forward and continues in soft tones.]

Say! wouldest thou? . . . it shall be as though thou didst sleep . . . with no awakening!

S. ANTHONY. [Repeats mechanically.] With no awakening?

DEATH. It shall be so! Thou shalt know no thought! Thou shalt feel nought! Thou shalt no more be anything!

[She sinks her chin on her right shoulder-blade and darts the black ray of her eyeless orbits; in her left hand, between her thumb and her first finger, she takes the hem of her shroud and raises it to the length of her arm, thus stretching it out to its full extent.]

S. ANTHONY. Nay, thou hast no need to play the mincing damsel before me! So oft have I pondered upon thee; verily I know thee well!

DEATH. No man knoweth me!

S. ANTHONY. Wherefore comest thou?

DEATH. To take thee!

S. ANTHONY. Is it mine hour?

DEATH. Ay, it is ever the hour!

[She draws near and stretches out her hand to him as though to aid him to rise. He crouches down, huddled against the wall.]

It will be swiftly ended! Come!

S. ANTHONY. [To himself.] Wherefore not?

DEATH. Give me thine hand! . . . Nay, thy finger alone! The tip of thy nail!

[S. Anthony draws his hand from under his armpit and slowly moves it towards Death.]

S. ANTHONY. But and if thy face were a lie? . . . were it but a change of being? . . . were I to have, down yonder, another body, should I yet have another soul or rather that which I have? . . . what do I know thereof? . . . Nay, nay! Art thou nothingness? Surely, thou art nothingness, in very truth? There is nought. Of a surety all is dark, there is no more!

DEATH. Ay! no more! That is the end! That is the last depth! How old soever be the cloth of my cloak, the daylight cannot pass through it. I will cast it about thy head. In that will I nail thee down. [She shows him the coffin.] Then shalt thou have lived for all the thousands of years that shall follow and for the eternity without end that shall follow, and when this wood shall be worn away and this linen shall be rotten, yet shall it be a long time since this little that remained of thee was no more.

I am the Comfortress, I am she who giveth sleep! As doth the mother to the little child who hath run about the whole day long, even so do I lay the sons of men to rest in their cradle, and I quench the candle.

They that despair, they that be tired, they that have loathing of all things, I have stayed their tears, I have given rest to their weariness, I have closed the yawning of their mouths, I have filled the void that was in them

. . . they that did mourn mourn no more, they that awaited are no more impatient . . . they have no more sense, they are brought to nought, they are melted away, they have gone up even as the dew of yesterday, they are brushed away even as the mark of the feet of the ostrich upon the sand, they are less than an echo that is lost ! . . .

S. ANTHONY. Thy breath is upon my face ! Thou dost smell of what is not and my soul is faint with the smell of thee.

DEATH. Down there shalt thou be without age, nor shalt thou have remembrance ; thou shalt have no past days, nor shall any thought for the days to come be with thee ; thou shalt be as young as the youngest and as old as the oldest, as strong as the most mighty and as fair as the most beautiful ! Come ! I am Peace ! I am the void that changeth not. . . . I am Knowledge of all things !

S. ANTHONY. [Leaping up.] Knowledge ? . . .

DEATH. If there be nought beyond me, shalt not thou, when thou dost possess me, have attained the last limit ? But and if there be a sun, or somewhat that may shine beyond the place of burial, if, as some say, I am but the threshold of eternity, then must thou take me if thou wouldest enjoy that, thou must pass across me if thou wouldest enter therein ! Whether there be nought or whether there be somewhat, if thy desire is toward what is not, come ! If thou dost desire blessed-ness, come ! If there be darkness or if there be light, if there be destruction or if there be rapture, whatever be the unknown, no more is it life ; then is this the better ! Away, let us go hence ! Give me thine hand ! Let us fly with the full speed of an horse unto my dominion of darkness !

> [S. Anthony rises and stretches forth his hands towards Death, when suddenly, behind her, appears Lust ; she passes her head over the shoulder of Death, she shows her face, and winks her eyes.]

LUST.   Wherefore shouldst thou die, O Anthony ?

DEATH.   Nay, wouldest thou still live ?

    [S. Anthony seats him again, and looks now at Death, now at Lust.]

LUST.   [Resumes.]   Dost thou even know it, this life that thou forsakest ?

DEATH.   Nay ! of a surety !   Thou art glutted therewith, thou hast disgust of it !

LUST.   Say it not !   Thou hast not tasted, the one after the other, the divers fruits of its raptures. . . . Know thou, O Anthony, that they that have wearied their hands for that they have pressed thereat with all their might, even these do weep, when their years come to an end, when they must needs forsake this joy withered whereto yet hung their worn-out strength !

DEATH.   Bah !   They are all alike, these thine earthly fruits !   From the first mouthful cometh loathing to the lips !

LUST.   [Takes her crown of roses from off her head and offers it to S. Anthony's nostrils.]   Look upon my fair roses !   I plucked them in the hedgerow, upon the trunk of an ash-tree, wherewith was entwined the eglantine.   The dew pearled the branches ; the lark sang, and the wind of the morning shook out the sweet smell of the green leaves . . . how fair is the world !   The world is very fair. . . . In the pastures that are full of grass the colts run joyously, the stallions neigh, the bulls bellow, they walk with heavy feet.   There be flowers whose stature is greater than thine ; they fill the seas with their sweet odours.   There be forests that wave upon the mountains, and lands where the incense doth smoke to the sun ; there be wide rivers and great seas.   Men fish in the rivers, they sail upon the seas.   In the time of the harvest the grapes are swollen, the thick drops sweat through the skin of the figs, the blood beateth, the sap floweth, the milk doth ring as it falleth into the vessels. . . .

Taste thou of this, of the life magnifical that is blessed
in all his days, even as the wheat hath flour in every
grain of his ear. Breathe the breath of the winds, sit
thee down under the citron trees, lie upon the moss,
bathe in the fountains. Drink wine, eat flesh, have thy
desire of women. Hold nature to thee with every lust
of thy being, and roll thee, even as a lover, upon her
broad bosom !
S. ANTHONY. [Reflecting.] Should I live ! . . .
DEATH. Nay, nay ! Life is evil ! The world is foul
of face !
S. ANTHONY. Ay ! peradventure were I wiser if I
die !
LUST. Thou dost speak of death ! Thou fool, thou
wouldst say unto thyself : " Ay, I know, I am wearied,
I have proved all things ! Therefore am I wise ! " . . .
then goest thou over all the earth, thou dost feed in the
pasture of sadness that thou mayest fatten thy pride !
Speak ! Say unto me ! . . . hast thou, some time, held
her upon thy knees, the laughing wanton, quivering,
her raiment undone ? She looked at herself in thine
eyes as in a mirror. Had she upon her skin the good
odours of withered violets, did her loins bend as palm-
trees, were her hands as running waters of desire that
did flood thee with longing when they passed over
thee ? Didst thou then leap upon her and seize her,
didst thou throw her back upon the bed and it sank as
the hollow of a wave ? She knit her arms about thee,
she held thee close, thou didst feel her sinews shaking,
her knees knocked together, her breasts were stiffened.
. . . Her head fell back, her body was loosened, she
lay as one who is worn with weariness, and the lids
of her dead eyes shivered as the wings of a moth . . .
Were ye content for that ye were alone ? . . . Did ye
laugh low as your flesh met ? Was thine heart strangely
softened for thankfulness, was it amazed, caught up in
her hair, and spread abroad therewith over her fair

naked limbs? Go to! Thou didst well! Therein is the goodness of life, the rest is but lies! . . .

*   *   *   *   *   *

Her dress is rose-coloured; it lieth low upon the neck; it claspeth her sleek shoulders. Her hair doth shine for its anointment; it is honey wherein is the smell of flowers. Thou shalt lay thine hand on her throat, thou shalt touch the great comb in her hair. For thee she shall strip her naked; she shall bare her feet; thou shalt see her vesture uplifted, her flesh shall be stretched out before thee. . . .

DEATH. Men pass staves beneath the bier; they depart. Look upon it, as thou dost follow it; it doth swing to the right and to the left, it plungeth, even as a boat, at every step. Death is therein and they bear her idly. The bearers sweat, the drops fall from their foreheads upon the coffin . . . the wheat is green, the pear-trees are all in flower, the hens cackle in the yard. The day is fair and the harvest will be good. Lo! the grave is ready. They wait; they lean them upon their mattocks. The earth doth crumble at the edge of the hole; it.poureth in at the corners. They come, they let thee down with ropes, the shovel is filled and the earth is thrown down, and it is as though nought had been!

LUST. [Passes swiftly beneath the arm of Death and seats her in front of S. Anthony. He looks at her and nods his head up and down. She says :] Yet in thine own despite there is that within the depth of thee that rageth furiously in rebellion. The heart of man is made for life. He doth breathe of it deeply wherever he be, from so far away as he is able. Here be the memories wherein he returneth and his hopes wherein he doth cast himself headlong, there be his possessions wherein he is at strife, yet hath he need of other worlds whose bounds are afar off, that he may run therein ever forward and move at his ease. So doth the craftsman of the quarries of marble fashion men therefrom; yet

another busieth him for folk that are no more known
upon earth; there be those that dream of happiness
for the folk that are not yet born. . . .
DEATH. [Pushes Lust to one side and again takes
her place.] What matter? Seeing that the multitudes
and their dreams, their hopes, their remembrance, the
imagination of their hearts and that which is real, shall
all be swallowed up in the same gulf! Where are they
now, all those women that were loved, they that put
on rings of gold to please their husbands; the virgins
with roseate cheeks who broidered upon cloth, and the
queens who were borne to the fountains under the
light of the moon? They had carpets, they had fans,
they had slaves; there were love songs played suddenly
behind walls. Their teeth shone, they bit deep in the
pomegranates; their vesture was loosened, the air
was sweet for the smell of it . . . where are the mighty
young men who ran so swiftly, who laughed so loud?
They had black beards, their eyes were alight. Where
is the wax of the torches that lit their feasting? Yea!
Men have passed away, and women and children, and
old men! There be great deserts where the red partridge
cannot find her food, yet were there great cities therein
aforetime . . . the chariots went about the streets,
men cried aloud in the open places! . . . I sat me
down upon the temples and they were overthrown!
With my shoulder I overturned the obelisks as I passed
by. I smote with my whip and I drove the nations
before me in terror as it were an herd of goats. One
couple and yet another couple have held speech about
me, alone, by the fireside whereof they stirred up the
ashes; they pondered what should they be hereafter.
But he that went cometh not again to tell unto his
fellows whether they were deceived aforetime, and
when they shall find one another in nothingness, no part
of them shall be known : it shall be with them even as
with the pieces of the log that burned before their eyes.

VI

(This page has no number, but it seems to be the continuation of the preceding passage.)

LUST. [Resumes.] Seest thou, yet afar off, where the branches are parted? There is a black shape that floweth upon the river! It is an Ethiopian bark; it is loaded with the feathers of the ostrich and with black women. They weep, they lift up their arms unto the sun, they look from the falls of the river unto the land where they were born. The ship is full of them, from the foot of the mast even to the bulwarks; the weight of the slaves doth lower it slowly even to the surface of the water, as it were a bunch of grapes that sinketh under the tide.

> [S. Anthony looks. Little by little the boat approaches; the women can be seen clearly.]

One there is; she is yet young, her lips are turned back even as the edges of a cup of coral. Her eyes are the colour of tin; they are empty even as the eyes of an idol; her great white teeth grin as though they were hungry. . . . Whistle unto her! She is ready to cast herself into the stream! She shall swim and thou shalt clasp her to thee, wet and naked; her smell is as the smell of the water, as it were a freshly-caught fish.

VII

(Pp. 274-5-6)

S. Anthony hears nothing more. The silence, as he listens, seems to him to increase, and the darkness is so deep, that he is amazed that he does not feel it resist him when he opens his eyes; yet it stifles him as though it were black marble moulded about his body.

After a time the shadows open, forming as it were two walls, and far beyond, at an incalculable distance, appears a city.

Clouds of smoke rise from the houses, tongues of fire writhe in the fog. Bridges of iron cross rivers of filth; carriages, closed as though they were coffins, encumber the long straight streets. Here and there women protrude their faces under the glimmer of the lights of taverns within which great mirrors shine. Men in hideous costume, grotesquely lean or obese, run as though they were being pursued, their chins lowered, their eyes aslant, seeming, every one of them, as though they were hiding something. And behold, in their midst S. Anthony perceives Jesus.

From long time of walking his body is bowed and his hair is white; his cross is plied to an immense arch upon his shoulder. It is too weighty; he calls aloud; none comes. He knocks at the doors; they remain closed. Ever he fares, imploring for a glance or a word of remembrance; none have time to listen to him; his voice is lost in the tumult; he totters and falls on his two knees. The rumour of his fall gathers together men of all nations, from the dwellers in Almaine even to the negroes; in the raving of their vengeance they howl in his ear :

189

" We have poured forth floods of human blood for thee, we have fashioned gags of thy cross, we have cloaked all hypocrisy beneath thy vesture, we have absolved all crimes in the name of thy mercy! Thou Moloch of the lamb's fleece, too long hath it lasted, thy passing! Die, die, and rise no more ! "

Then others, they that loved him, the furrows of whose tears are yet on their cheeks, say to him : " How long have we not prayed, wept, hoped ! Cursed be thou for our long endurance, for our hearts unassuaged ! "

A king smites him with his sceptre and accuses him for that he exalted the lowly; the people tear him with their nails and cast it in reproach to him that he sustained princes. Some bow them down before him in mockery; others spit in his face, in no wrath, merely from habit. Merchants ask him to sit down in their shops. The Pharisees allege that he is cumbering the way. The doctors probe his wounds, and pretend that none should believe therein; the philosophers say: " It was but a phantom."

Men do not even look at him. None know him. He lies in the mire and the rays of the wintry sun strike on his dying eyes.

The life of the world continues around him ; the carriages splash him, harlots brush against him with the hem of their gowns. The idiot, as he passes, flings his laughter at him; the murderer casts his crime in his face, the drunkard his vomit, the poet his song. The crowd trample upon him and crush him—and at the last, when is left on the pavement nothing save his great crimson heart whose beating dies away, little by little, men hear—not the great and bitter cry of Calvary—but only a faint sigh, hardly a breath. . . . The shadows close again.

S. ANTHONY.   Horror ! Nought, nought, surely, O my God, I have seen nought.   What could be, after ?

[He kneels down.]

NOTES

NOTES

A WHOLE volume of annotations might be written upon the many remarkable personages and ideas that figure in the Temptation of S. Anthony; I have, however, thought it best to confine myself to a minimum. I have cited analogies here and there where they seemed to throw some light upon the text, I have noted what seemed to be errors on the part of the writer, and I have given the various Gnostic and other words for which I attempt English equivalents. Those who wish to make a thorough study of the book will find full scope for research in the list of authorities consulted by Flaubert, and cited in the second appendix. [For Gnosticism especially I would refer them to Mr. C. W. King's book, "The Gnostics and their remains" (David Nutt).] This list, it is true, applies to the 1874 MS. rather than to the other, but without question many of the authorities must have been consulted for both versions.

Epigraph on page 2 (also on p. 213, Appendix I.).
  " Messers Demons
  " Pray you, let me be ! "
The French is—
  " Messieurs les démons
  " laissez-moi donc ! "
Messer is, strictly speaking, Venetian; it seems, however, legitimate in this case.
Text (page 3).
  " The Hermit and his convent."
Those who wish for a sketch of the part S. Anthony

o

played in the Christianity of his day—A.D. 305,—have but to refer to Gibbon's "Decline and Fall of the Roman Empire" (chap. xxxvii.). S. Anthony and his friend and master, S. Paul, are considered as pioneers of the Coptic Church, and even to the present day the Coptic Patriarch is usually chosen from the monastery founded by these two Saints near the Red Sea. There are two curious pictures, the one of S. Anthony being tempted in the desert, the other of a visit paid by him to S. Paul, in S. Peter's in Rome, in the room known as Cardinal Rampolla's Sacristy, famous for the Melozzo da Forli frescoes which it contains.

Page 3. "A painting of the Blessed Virgin." The text has "image" which might be either image (statuette) or picture; the latter is far more likely here, supported as it is by the passage on p. 5;—"graven outward, as an image," *i.e.* suggesting that it is flat and might be in relief. Probably a small picture of the early Byzantine eikon type.

Page 5. "I behold my lusty body in the pools as it were in a mirror." Another ambiguity; "figure" (text) may also mean face, but the pig goes on to mention his paws and his belly; "silhouette" would be the exact word.

The pig is, throughout the book, a curious echo of his sainted master, a reproving parody, as it were, of S. Anthony's vainer moments, a reflection in an ignoble mirror of certain troubled phases; now and again he asserts his own individuality, in wonderment or fear, wishing for the wings of the pig of Clazomenae (p. 108), or crying aloud in horror at sacrilege when the Avenging Maidens appear (p. 207); to my thinking M. Bertrand is less than just to his rather engaging personality. It is notable that the pig is ruthlessly excluded from the 1874 edition.

Page 7. "The City of the Sun on the Nile."
The remains of Heliopolis (Matarieh), the city of the

Sun, are actually some miles from the Nile, though quite close to the present Ismailia Canal, which occupies practically the site of the ancient canal which took off opposite Memphis and connected that city with Suez : this canal—first conceived by Sesostris, according to Pliny—by Tutis (or Titus) of Memphis, for Hagar the mother of Ishmael, according to Makrizy—was known in Moslem days as the Khalig el Masri, and the small remaining section which actually ran through Cairo was only filled up a few years ago.

Page 9. "On the cool stones of the sanctuaries." " Basiliques " in text; a thoroughly Byzantine touch. In Jean Lombard's curious and admirable work, " Byzance," there are several most excellent illustrations of Basilica by Auguste Leroux.

Page 11. ANGER. " Thou shouldest have had a heavy sword." This passage occurs again in the first fragment (p. 172), as do the two following passages put into the mouths of Pride and Logic. The fragment was certainly well worth preserving for its fine imagery.

Page 12. " Rather is it a death-bed." Text, " Une agonie,"—almost always used of the last moments of a dying man.

Page 18. (Description of Anger.) " Her arms end in two leaden balls." Sir Gaston Maspero suggested to me that this might mean " clenched gauntlets," which would give just that effect; at any rate no part of the actual body of Anger is visible; she is wholly covered with armour.

Page 19. The curious tenets of the Paternians—not uncommendable in their way—suggest a striking analogy to the chief feature of Pharaonic art from which this sect may well have derived their inspiration. In Pharaonic art only the upper part of the human body can be really called life-like and beautiful; all below the waist is dead and conventional, though extremely accurate in many cases; the ancient Egyptians portrayed not the living man, but the Osirian; hence, when those organs to which the Paternians had so strong an objection are portrayed at all, the reason for their presence is worship or symbolism. The parts of the body assigned by this sect to the Devil would, in any case, be quite unnecessary in the Osirian world.

Page 20. "The Tertullianists." Flaubert wrote "Tertullanists," evidently a slip, but worth noting in view of one or two other curious anomalies in his text.

Page 21. "The Gnostics." I have paraphrased nearly all the Gnostic words, and I give the list of them here. Gnosticism throws a most interesting light upon the whole of the "Temptation."

Page 21. "The Ages." Text, "Les Aeons."

"The Maker of Nations." Text, "Le Démiurge."

"Him who ruleth the world." Text, "Cosmocrator."

Page 21. "Man." Text, "Antropos" (sic "Anthropos").

Page 23. "Par la vertu de Satan." Text, cf. "the virtue is gone out of me"; but "strength" seems more apposite than "virtue" in the case of the Evil One.

Pages 21–23. "The Abysm." Text, "Bythos."

"The Comforter." Text, "Paraclete."

"Belief." Text, "Pistis."

"Wisdom." Text, "Sophia."

(The Pistis-Sophia is the Gnostic gospel.)

"The Perfected." Text, "Teletos."

"Yokes." Text, "Syzygies."

"Fulfilment." Text, "Plérôme."

Page 26. "The Beingless." Text, "Haën-soph" (Ensoph). (A Cabalistic word.)

Page 27. "Understanding." Text, "Ennoia," the companion of Simon Magus.

Page 27. "The sky green as a sapphire." Text, "un ciel vert comme du saphir."

Page 29. "Grace." Text, "Charis."

"Silence." Text, "Σιγὴ."

"Barbelo." This barbelo is quite a different personage to the Barbelo (often called Barbelus), he was the son of Baal; Barbelo here is the Heavenly mother of the Saviour; the Gnostics could not accept Mary, the earthly mother, as sufficing for the birth of Godhead.

Page 32. The Carpocratians suggest the Buddhist doctrine of the wheel, to a certain degree, and the gradual purification of the soul after undergoing the cycle of all human phases.

Page 32. "Concupiscence." Text, "Prounicos" (Prunicos).

Page 35. "The great hounds." Text, "Molosses," *i.e.* mastiffs.

Page 38. "Circoncellions." Cf. the Car of Juggernaut and other fakirs' practices.

Page 39. "The Anointment of the dying." "Viatique," the viaticum, originally the food given to monks when about to set forth on a journey.

Page 40. APOLLONIUS. "His fair locks, severed by a parting, even as those of Christ." King has a note on this; "What proves the want of any real authority for the portraits of the Saviour is the fact that the earliest monuments in sculpture or painting represent him as a youth and beardless"; probably the convention of the time, "after the fashion of the Nazarenes," as a friend suggested to me. There is a most interesting account of "Apollonius the Revivalist," in Professor Flinders Petrie's "Personal Religion in Egypt before Christianity." see p. 193

Page 43. "O Gods!" A saying of his was "O Gods, grant me few possessions and no wants."

Page 45. "We beheld a demon." Text, "empuse," a species of Gorgon. The translator of the 1874 edition, which contains this passage, renders "a wild horse"; apparently the context misled him.

Page 45. "Phraotes" this should be, not "Phraortes."

Page 47. "Sesostris." It would be interesting to know whether Flaubert meant Rameses the Great or the

third Usertsen (Sanouosrit); a much-discussed point.
Popular feeling supports the former, but the majority
of Egyptologists are for the latter view.

Page 50. Petrie thinks it certain that Apollonius never
met Nero.

Page 52. "The Receivers of Contention." These are
the Cabiri, sons of Ptah (Hephæstus); they figure
largely in Gnosticism.

The Phœnicians adored the seven Chaldæan planets
under the name of the Cabiri, and attributed the
chieftainship of the seven to Eschmoun the Pole Star,
the one and only compass of that hardy race of navigators.
(Péladan—Les idées et les formes.)

Page 53. "The blind horse-footed folk crush with
their feet the plant of the further seas." Text, "Les
hippopodes cassent avec leurs pieds la plante d'outremer."
The "hippopodes" were apparently a semi-human
race, and not animals. "Outremer" is "ultramarine"
according to the dictionaries, but as ultramarine seems
to have been made from lapis lazuli, I venture in this
instance, where it is distinctly a vegetable and not a
mineral, to prefer my paraphrase.

Page 54. "The tamer of men." "Androdamas."
"The wayfarer's ward." "Xeneston." Here it is a
talisman, but it suggests a passport or firman given to
Apollonius by the Parthian king, Phraotes. Flaubert
gives a miraculous aspect and colouring to the whole
of the episode.

Page 55. "Aphrodite . . . of the form of a cone at
Paphos." This recalls the attempt of Heliogabalus to
introduce into Rome the phallic worship of the black
cone of Emesa; Jean Lombard's " L'Agonie " gives a
most interesting account of it.

The whole question raises a vast region of discussion
on meteorite statues, the conical form in phallic worship,
black Virgins, &c. . . .; it should be remembered that
this subject, nowadays relentlessly banned from all

open discussion, was, for all antiquity, one of the
foundation-stones of all worship. To us it may seem
obscene; to them it was vital.

Page 55. Names of Aphrodite. Here again I have
paraphrased. " Aphrodite of the Heavens, who foreseeth, Astarte that rageth, Aphrodite that turneth
away "; in the text these are " Vénus Uranienne;
Aphrodite Prévoyante, Astarté Furieuse, Vénus
Apostrophienne."

Page 55. " The dice of Athene." " Les skirapies de
Minerve."

Page 58. " The Sacred Chair." Text, " Bhéma "
(the Rostrum).

 " The Ordinances." Text, " Principes."

 " Vessels." Text, " Vases." Manes was called the
Vessel of election.

 " The Shoulderer." Text, " Omophorus."

 " He that holdeth in glory." Text, " Splendi-
tenens."

 " Knowledge." Text, " Gnose " (the Gnosis).

Page 58. " Penitence doth brighten her life unto her."
" Aviver," the word in the text, is rendered in the
average dictionary—and that includes a large proportion
of the more costly French-English Lexicons—by the
word " burnish "; but this eliminates the " vie, vivre "
element which is undoubtedly paramount. Un-
questionably the real meaning is, as Sir Gaston Maspero
pointed out to me, " to restore and strengthen the ' life,'
and make it more brilliant." This combines the ideas
of life and brightness and, above all, the sense of
restoring to anything its special life and functions.

II

Page 61. Text, " Ciseler les Plats." It seems
difficult to attribute any other meaning, but one might
almost have expected some phrase about preparing
dainties,—plates rather than plate.

Page 63. FAITH. " Believe that which thou seest
not." This whole passage throws a curious light on the
difference between the tenets of Protestantism and
those of the Roman Church. According to the latter
faith has nothing to do with human reason; and, after
all, human reason can hardly claim the right to pro-
nounce upon things divine, unless we accept, as the
basis of all religions, the Heraclitan axiom that, " men
make to themselves gods in their own image." Men
necessarily " think in relations," and though they may
speculate with intelligence and probability on what the
Deity would or should do, were He in their place, they
cannot fairly suppose that such speculations are records
of facts or certainties; that were too much like an
attempt to measure up Heaven with a foot-rule. When
men attempt to determine the Infinite, the result they
usually attain is the indefinite.

Page 66. [Variant.] " That they may the better
brighten the life unto Love Celestial." Text, " aviver."

Page 67. " We pass in great courses about the heavens."
Text, " Nous décrivons dans les cieux de gigantesques
paraboles." Compare " The stars in their courses."

Page 69. " The dim heaven of fire of the wise men."
Text, " L'empyrée vague des philosophes."

Page 73. " Loose strife." Text, " Lysimachia."

Page 73. "The pinewood tablets that constrain my waist."
A tribute to the longevity and universality of the corset.

Page 74. "The firestone of Egypt that preventeth childbirth." Text, "L'ecbolada d'Égypte qui préviént les accouchements."
"Preventeth" can here mean "prevent" either in the modern sense of "warding off," or in the older sense "warning," "going before," as in the prayer-book "prevent and follow us." The French word, and also the sense of the whole passage, can convey either meaning.

Page 74. "My little Syracusan hound." Text, "roquet," properly a pug dog, but usually applied to any small yapping cur. "Brachet" was a very tempting rendering, the more so from the consideration that Meleager's Phanion kept a tame hare; why should not Demonassa have a tame greyhound? But Malory's word seemed too remote from the period of English that suggested itself to me for this work. I might remark, in this connection, that all the Demonassa episode and also that about the Muses are anything but biblical or even semi-biblical in their possibilities, so far as phraseology is concerned.

Page 74. "Hermione," according to one dictionary, is a small town in Elis, so called after one of the many names of Demeter.

Page 76. "The Bibasis of the Dorians." Apparently a Spartan dance for boys and girls, in which the chief aim was to kick oneself behind as high as possible; but there is a curious suggestion in the word βιβάζω of lasciviousness, which at first sight one would hardly associate with the stern dwellers in Lacedemonia. The context also about the striped skirt suggests somehow that Flaubert had not verified his allusions; the Spartans, it is true, were originally Dorians. Students of ancient Greek dances may be able to throw light upon this as upon the "martypsa" about which so far I have been unable to obtain any information. I owe this note on Bibasis to the kindness of two contributors to "Notes and Queries."

Page 76. "The harp of Egypt with the forty golden chords." Text, "épigonion." In M. Jean Capart's book on Egyptian Art there is an admirable representation of what should be an épigonion—an " angle harp " with the player bending over it. (Planche 90.)

Pages 79, 80. "Hirah of Adulla and Tamar." Flaubert has not kept rigidly to the text as we know it in our authorised version (Genesis xxxviii. 12) ; I have ventured to take that text as it stands. Later on, in the passage, he speaks of " un cercle d'airain qu'il retire de sa tête." This I have rendered " circlet." The authorised version has " bracelets," which could not suit the French context.

Page 86. The bells on the queen's parasol are described in the text as " clochettes vermeilles." " Vermeil," according to Larousse, is : (1) a small worm ; (2) a brilliant dye (cochineal) ; (3) a red varnish used to give brilliancy to gilding ; (4) silvergilt.

It might be here either vermilion (though one is inclined to question how that would harmonise with the green and white of the parasol), or else silver- or copper-gilt. The use of the word " clochettes " is curious ; one would rather have expected " grelots."

Page 88. "Here is gum and cinnamon and silfy." " Du ladanon et du cinnamone et du silphium." Silphium—probably assafœtida—is still highly esteemed in the East for sauces.

Page 89. "The buckler of Djian-ben-Djian who builded the Pyramids." The Djinns—an obvious suggestion to the Oriental mind. The statement is rather on a par with that of Richard Johnson, the Elizabethan, who asserts that the Great Pyramids were in Greece.

Page 89. "Ah, didst thou know what I have in my little box." The actual text has " si tu avais," which is a misprint for " si tu savais."

Page 89. "It was upon a night wherein the king Solomon lost his wit for desire of me." According to the Abyssinian tradition, Solomon showed singular acumen on this occasion; he had invited the queen to a special banquet, at which he provided highly-spiced food but rather unsatisfying drink; he placed his pavilion at her disposal for the night, with the proviso that she should touch nothing in any of the rooms adjoining her bedroom. To this she agreed, but, during the night, her overpowering thirst compelled her to explore the whole pavilion furtively in search of water; just as she found a waterjar and was lifting it to her lips, the king appeared and reminded her of the proviso and the consequent penalty; the case might be rendered exactly in French by the expression " elle avait parié une discrétion." She acknowledged the claim, but insisted upon sufficient respite to allow of her assuaging her thirst; this done, she acquiesced in the situation. The Abyssinians allege that this was the foundation of their present reigning dynasty.

Page 90. " Catch fish in my vivers." Text, " viviers " (fish-ponds). " Vivers " is an attractive suggestion, the more so for its misleading resemblance to the word " vivres."

Page 93. " Hopping." Text, " sautillant à cloche-pied." Either hopping or hobbling, or both together.

Page 96. The Sphinx and the Labyrinth. It was supposed, probably with much truth, that there was a secret passage from the Sphinx up to the Pyramid temples, used for various trials of initiates. Any book on magic will give some kind of account of these, in which the symbolic form and supposed attributes of the Sphinx played a prominent part.

Page 96. " Thou shalt never melt the ' stone ' of me." Text, " granit." A necessary compromise; the Sphinx is hewn out of the local sandstone. The Sphinx temple (probably a far later monument) is of granite; also, not so many years ago, only the blackened head of the Sphinx was visible—two misleading factors. Of course Flaubert may have taken the idea from one of the many granite sphinxes, for example, the Louvre red granite sphinx, but he must have meant the great Sphinx here. It must be remembered that Flaubert wrote the 1848 version before he had visited Egypt.

Page 98. "Porsenna and the bells." It seems curious to assign this to the Chimera. It is said that within the enclosure of the labyrinth of King Porsenna at Clusium there were fourteen Pyramids.

Pages 99, 100. "The mouthless folk, the half-folk, the shade-footed folk, the Blemmyes, the dog-headed folk." All these are to be found in Mandeville and kindred writers. Text, "Astomi, Nisnas, Sciapodes, Blemmyes, Cynocephali"; modern research has disillusioned them into mere memories of tribes of Ethiopia. The Blemmyes (possibly the Barabras of Southern Ethiopia) are the folk "whose heads do grow beneath their shoulders"; the Nisnas present some interest; the Arabic dictionaries say (1) fabulous people who have only one foot, (2) monkeys (popular). "Half-folk" was suggested to me by the two Arabic words, Nis or Nuss (half), and Nas (folk).

Page 101. "It is my sport to break with mine horn the faces of the kings that are graven upon the mountain." One cannot help thinking of the (second) broken colossus at Abou-Simbel, though its fall is more probably due to lapse of time and settlement than to any horned attack.

Pages 103, 104. The Mantichora and the Down-Looker. Text, "le Martichoras et le Catoblepas." The Mantichora (a fabulous creature, now extinct), in his active opposition to armed exploration of the desert, recalls the fate of the Persian army sent into the Western desert of Egypt, via the Oasis of Kharga (the temple of Hibis there is perhaps the only survival of a century of foreign occupation). Kharga was the last landmark of civilisation that they saw; they fell, fifty thousand of them, a prey to the desert—or to the Mantichora?

III

Page 121. LUST. " Ay, and there be dead women " . . .
A strange passage; one would say that Lust foresees
the exhaustion of the possibilities of nudity, and hints
that she can offer a species of nudity that suggests even
more than itself !

Page 122. " And even in love crowned." The same
expression occurs on p. 174 (fragment II). Text,
" amour heureux," obviously wedded love.

Page 126. " Follows the idol of ' Tartary,' a statue of a
man in ' green ' agate ; in his hand he holds seven featherless arrows." It is curious that this is the exact
description of the idol Hebal, in the Caaba, at Mecca,
with one difference, that according to Gibbon, Hebal
is of " red " agate ; the arrows are the symbols of divina-
tion. Had Flaubert made some confusion ? He goes on
to speak of the 360 idols of the Arabians, and says
nothing more about Tartary. Gibbon, moreover, was
one of his books of reference.

Page 126. " Flowers of the fig-tree." Text, " Fleurs du
pipalas," the Indian pepul.

Page 129. " As though I should spew forth the lives
that travail in my stomach." Text, " vomir la digestion
de mes existences." It suggests the Buddhist doctrine
of the Wheel, and the thought that however many lives
a man or a god may go through, all those lives are
intertwined and interdependent.

Page 130. " Were I to dig the pits of the Pagada for
ever." I have found no satisfactory explanation of
Pagada ; there is a lake in Central Africa of that name.
Allatius (liber quorundam Græcorum) renders " a well
of madness."

Page 133. "Thou Ferver, thou first soul." Ferouer, in Zoroastrianism is the Pre-existing Soul.

Page 134. "Apis." The "sacred words" are the key-note of the Pharaonic as of many other religions. Not only were there special words but they had to be recited with special intonation and in a special order; any mistake invalidated the ceremony and entailed recommencement. There were special sacred phrases, for example, in the temple feasts wherein the statue of the God, previous to exposition, had to be brought to life, so to speak, before it could eat—or, rather, "touch and remit"—the sacred offerings; the God was then, again with special phrases, restored to a mute existence in the sanctuary. At Abydos Seti 1. is represented with his little son Rameses II. behind him, ready to "prompt" him, suggestive of a "server" at Mass. Seti's own temple, by the way, at Thebes, is a vivid presentment of the words that follow, "silent under the sunlight except for the chattering sparrows, and white with their droppings."

The Sanctuary of Apis was of course Sakkara.

Page 137. "The maids winked their eyes as they passed by the bushes." Text, "cligner," which may mean "blink," or "wink"; it might express either fear or acquiescence—or the combination of both, as found in the threadbare jape about the Bois de Boulogne in French comic papers of a certain class. There is also a tempting analogy of sound between Saturn and Satyr.

Page 139. "From the Beetle even to the Thunderer." A Scarab with wings was the recognised Gnostic name of the Creator. In Pharaonic mythology Kheper-Ra was the Beetle of Eternity, also called "Atum"; Atum was the sunset name and Kheper-Ra the dawn name of Ra. Atum is another form of the Syrian Adon (Lord) = Adonis.

Page 142. "The robe worn in the Mysteries." Text,

"la robe usée des mystères." Sufficiently ambiguous! It may mean "worn out in the Mysteries," and then given over to the young matrons, or "in use in the Mysteries," and lent for swaddling.

Page 143. "Neleus, king of Pisa, Eurytus, king of Œchalia." Text, "Nélée, roi de Pise, 'Euryle,' roi d'Œchalie." "Euryle" is a misprint for "Eurytus," from whom Hercules took the big black bow that eventually came into the hands of Odysseus, who alone could bend it.

"Pisa" looks suspicious. Neleus, the father of Nestor, was surely lord of Pylos (though there is a Pisa in Elis which may have had some connection with his family: at any rate I have left Pisa).

Page 148. The title of the high priest of Cybele is "Archi-Gallus," which is actually the word in the French text.

Page 150. "Derceto" is "Atergatis." "Oannes" is the fish-god of the Babylonians; Oannes is also, according to the Assyrians, the first man. For an interesting and amusing description of him, consult Voltaire Dictionnaire Philosophique; "Catéchisme Chinois, 4me entretien." Cu-Su (loq) "Les Prêtres Chaldéens s'étaient avisés d'adorer les brochets de l'Euphrate. Ils prétendaient qu'un fameux brochet, nommé Oannes leur avait autrefois appris la théologie, que ce brochet était immortel, qu'il avait trois pieds de long et un petit croissant sur la queue." The whole passage is too long to cite here but is well worth reading. Péladan says (Les Idées et les Formes): "A curious Messiah, Ea Khan (Oannes) an Amphibious God, came to teach mankind. At sunset he plunged again into the sea; this signifies that civilisation was brought by some stranger to the aboriginal race"— or, perhaps, simply that the sun rose to light the world and at eve gave place to the night, "when no man can work."

Pages 150, 151. Names of gods and goddesses. Here, as with the Gnostic words, I have paraphrased, I give the list :

Page 150.   The Deliveress : " Ilythia."

Pages 150, 151.   The Maidens Avengers : " Potniades."
The Saviour of Cities : " Sosipolis."
The Pure Ones : " Cathares."
The Forager : " Laphria."
The Chantress : " Hymnia."
The Fire-bearer : " La Pyronienne."
The Midwife : " L'Accoucheuse."
The Huntress : " La Chasseresse."
The Healer : " La Salutaire."
The Light-bearer : " Lucifère."
The Mistress of Harbours : " La Patronne des Ports."
" A necklace of marigolds." Text, " chrysanthèmes."

Page 152.   The Lord of Landmarks : " Terminus."
Anna of the years that pass : " Anna Perenna."

" Marigolds " was a suggestion made to me ; it seemed far more suitable, and I believe that it is not incorrect from a botanical point of view. Chrysanthemum would be an anachronism both to Diana and to Biblical language.

Page 154.   The Prophetess : " Pythia."
Rose - laurels : " Lauriers - roses " ; strictly " oleanders."

Page 155.   Mimallon : " She that rageth."   " Sileni." One usually thinks of Silenus as one particular individual, a ribald Sancho Panza to Dionysus.

Page 158.   " I made sport unto myself with the ensigns of the Gods."   " Je me jouais avec les attributs des dieux."   " Attributs " is " emblems," undoubtedly ; one can imagine a double idea ; Cupid would borrow the club of Hercules and play at being a strong man, or the lyre of Apollo and make Olympus resonant with music.

Page 158. "Mammon." Text, "Plutus."

Page 158. (The Gods of the Hearth.) "Great families." Text, "De longues familles": the usual cry, the rate of race-increase diminishing with the downfall of the race.

Page 160. "The women anointed themselves . . . they sought out the captains, they cut off their heads." Cf. Judith and Holofernes: especially does Botticelli's picture occur to the mind.

Page 161. "Against the door of the hut." Text has "la cabane de la porte,"—an unintentional inversion.

Page 166. "The body of Cleopatra." A few years ago the Paris letter of the "Daily Telegraph" cited an account of Cleopatra's grave, vouched for by an anonymous writer who stated that the sarcophagus, proved to contain the body by inscriptions thereon, rests in the Bibliothèque Nationale under a glass case that contains medals. The sarcophagus had been brought over to Paris by a French savant some forty years before and placed in the National Library. It had been found impossible to preserve the mummy, and the authorities had decided to bury it quietly in the little old bit of garden enclosed in the building; and there Cleopatra was laid to rest secretly fifty years ago. I found this account quoted in Mr. Douglas Sladen's "Queer things about Egypt" (pp. 181, 182). Mr. Sladen thinks it was more likely that the mummy (which should not have been hard to preserve) was so buried owing to the notorious ill-luck that accompanied it; he adds that one can hardly, in such a connection, endorse the lines:

"It is well done and fitting for a princess
    Descended of so many royal kings."

Page 178. "The rain from the gutters hath trickled

P

down our backs, all the despair of life hath poured through our souls."

> " Il pleut dans mon cœur
>   Comme il pleut dans la rue."
>   (Verlaine.)

Page 189. "The Dwellers in Almaine." Text, "Les Germains." Mandeville's word was too tempting to neglect.

APPENDIX

APPENDIX

I. NOTE ON THE MANUSCRIPTS OF THE "TEMPTATIONS OF S. ANTHONY"

Apart from the numerous covers containing the drafts there are in existence three entirely distinct manuscripts.

1. The 1849 manuscript.

Flaubert must have started on "S. Anthony" on his return from Italy, in the course of the summer of 1845. After three years of reading and preparatory labour he began the actual writing in May 1848.

The cardboard cover which contains the manuscript—full of erasures and corrections !—has on the outside the following note : " May 1848, September 1849," and the epigraph :

> " Messers Demons
> " Pray you, let me be ! " (repeated twice).

The manuscript contains 541 pages. At the foot of the last page Flaubert writes : " Here endeth the Temptation of Saint Anthony.—Wednesday the 12th of September 1849, at 3h. 20m. after noon, of a sunny windy day. Commenced on Wednesday the 24th of May 1848, at a quarter past 3."

It is this manuscript that was read to Louis Bouilhet and Maxime Du Camp.

2. The 1856 manuscript.

This is the preceding manuscript, very much curtailed and ordered. It is far more carefully prepared, and though erasures and corrections are still frequent, as in

all Flaubert's final manuscripts, it was apparently ready
to be sent to press.

It contains only 193 pages.

The cardboard cover bears the same epigraph as that
of the preceding manuscript: " Messers Demons . . ."
and it has this date, " Autumn 1856."

It is the text of this manuscript, as it stands, that we
have published in the present volume.

3. The 1874 manuscript.

This is the version known to the public. It has been
completely remodelled, and differs widely, both in
spirit and in composition, from the two preceding
manuscripts.

We may note that before the publication of this last
version three fragments of the " Temptation " appeared
in " l'Artiste," in 1857 :

Sixth series, 2nd issue : Nebuchadnezzar ; the Queen of
Sheba.

Sixth series, 5th issue : Apollonius of Tyana.

Sixth series, 8th issue : The Sphinx and the Chimera ;
the fabulous beasts.

Quite a study might be made—no critic has seriously attempted this—of the sources of the "Temptation of S. Anthony."

However, pending such an event, we think it incumbent on us to publish here the list of the works that Flaubert read or consulted for the 1874 version. This list was made out by Flaubert himself, and we reproduce it word for word, with the bibliographical explanations that we owe to Dr. Paul Dorveaux, the learned librarian of the University of Paris.

Evidently this catalogue only represents a meagre portion of Flaubert's reading; but it should be quite possible for any one who studies his drafts and his project closely, to re-discover the traces of his work between 1845 and 1848. That task we leave to whoever may, some day, bring out the edition of the 1849 manuscript.

Page 1 of Flaubert's manuscript.

Saint Anthony.—From the beginning of July 1870 to the 26th of June 1872.

I have read, for the "Temptation of Saint Anthony," the following works :

[BLACK NOTE-BOOK.]

" Note on the God Homa."—Burnouf.

This " note " was published in volumes 4 sqq. of the 4th series of the " Journal Asiatique " (1844, &c.). It forms a part of a work by Eugène Burnouf entitled " Etudes sur la langue et les textes zends " which was issued separately in 1850.

" Religion of the Aryas," Maury, for the Soma.

Note published by Alfred Maury in the "Revue Archéologique" (Vols. IX. and X., 1852–1853), also issued separately (Paris, 1853) under the following title : "Essai historique sur la Religion des Aryas, pour servir à éclaircir les origines des religions hellénique, latine, gauloise, germaine et slave."

Layard, for Ormuz. *)

Layard (Austen). "Nineveh and its Remains." London, Murray, 1849. Two vols., large octavo.

"Fragments of Chaldæan Astrology."—Hoefer.

Dr. Ferdinand Hoefer published, in 1852, the volume of "L'Univers Pittoresque" devoted to the following countries : Chaldæa, Assyria, Media, Babylonia, Mesopotamia, &c. He is the author of a "Histoire d'Astronomie" (Paris, Hachette, 1873, 12mo.).

"Hell." "The Deluge," Maury.

Alfred Maury published the articles "Enfer" and "Déluge" in the "Encyclopédie Moderne," edited by Léon Renier (Paris, 1848).

"Death." Maury.

Alfred Maury published "Le Personnage de la Mort" in the "Revue Archéologique."

Zoëga. Extracts from the Coptic manuscripts.

Zoëga (Georg). "Catalogus codicum Copticorum manuscriptorum." Romæ, 1810, Small in fol.

Apocryphal animals. "British Review."

Natural history of apocryphal animals, "British Review," June number, 1835, pp. 264–292.

"Saint Basil." Hexameron.

"Saint Basil the Great, Explanation of the six days work." ('Εξαμέρον) ; letters and discourses. Greek text annotated. Paris, Garnier frères, 1852. 12mo.

Ritter. "Ancient Philosophy, for Anaxagoras."

Ritter (Henri). "Histoire de la Philosophie Ancienne," translated from the German by J. Tissot. Paris, 1836–1837. 4 vols. in fol.

Thevet.—"Universal Cosmography."

*) Dont remember Ormuz in this text.

Thevet (F. André). "Cosmographie Universelle."
Paris, P. Lhuillier, 1575. 2 vols. in fol.
" Prodigious Histories by Boaistruau."
Boaistruau (Pierre). "Histoires prodigieuses extraites
des plus fameux auteurs grecs et latins." Paris, 1597–
1598. 6 vols. in fol.
" Hortus sanitatis."
Anonymous Latin treatise on materia medica, divided
into four parts : (1) Botany ; (2) Zoology ; (3) Minera-
logy ; (4) Urines. Published in Germany in the Fifteenth
Century ; it has been translated into French.
" Treatise on Monsters."—Sorbin.
Sorbin (Arnaud). "Tractatus de Monstris." Paris,
1570. 12mo.
" Marvellous History of Plants."—Duret.
Duret (Claude). "Histoire admirable des Plantes et
herbes esmerveillables et miraculeuses en nature." Paris,
Nicolas Buon, 1605. 8vo.

ANCIENT TOPOGRAPHY.

" The Imperial Palace of Constantinople."—Labarte.
Labarte (Jules). " Le Palais Impérial de Constantine et
ses abords ; Sainte-Sophie, le forum Augustéon et
l'hippodrome, tels qu'ils existaient au Xme siècle."
Paris, Didron, 1861, quarto.
" Alexandria " (note on). La Père.
" Egypt and Alexandria."—Strabo.
" Geography " of Strabo, translated from Greek into
French by La Porte du Theil, Gosselin, Coray & Letronne,
Paris, " Imprimerie impériale," 1805–1819, 5 vols., quarto.
" Abbreviated History of Philostorgus."—Photius.
" History of the Church," by Philostorgus, abbreviated
by Photius, translated from Greek into Latin by Henry
Valois. Paris, 1673.
" Ancient Egypt."—Champollion-Figeac.
Volume of the collection entitled : " L'Univers Pitto-
resque ; Afrique," vol. I.

⸢ " Procopius on Buildings, for Constantinople."
Procopius, " Treatise on Buildings Constructed or Re-
paired under the auspices of Justinian," translated from
Greek into Latin by the Jesuit Claud Maltretus. Paris,
1663.
Manuscript Letter of Heuzey, on Alexandria.
Leon Heuzey, member of the " Institut " (Académie des
inscriptions et belles lettres), professor at " l'école des
Beaux Arts," curator of antiquities at the Louvre
Museum, &c.
Manuscript Letter of F. Baudry, on the Egyptian Bean.
Frédéric Baudry, man of letters and philologist, assistant
curator at the Bibliothèque Mazarine, formerly librarian
at the Bibliothèque de l'Arsenal, &c.

Jews.

" The Kabbala."—Franck.
Franck (Adolphe). " La Kabbale, ou la philosophie
religieuse des Hebreux," Paris, Hachette, 1843. 8vo.
" Oriental Studies."—Franck.
Franck (Adolphe). " Etudes Orientales," Paris, Lévy
frères, 1861. 8vo.
" Critical Study of the Bible."—Michel Nicolas.
Nicolas (Michel). " Etudes critiques sur la Bible."
Paris, Lévy frères, 1861–1863. 2 vols., 8vo.
" The immortality of the soul in Hebrew thought." Obry.
Obry (J.-B.-F.) on the immortality of the soul according
to the Hebrews, in " Mémoires de l'Académie d'Amiens,"
in the year 1839, p. 471.
" Customs of the Jews."—Barnier.
" Political and Rural Economy."—Regnier.
⸰ " Mischna."
" Mischna, sive totius Hebraeorum juris, rituum, antiqui-
tation ac legum oralium systema, cum Maimonidis
et Bartenorae commentariis . . . latinitate donavit Guil.
Surenhusius." Amsterdam, 1698–1703, 6 vols. in fol.
" Moses."—Pastoret. (Flaubert has written " Moyse.")

Pastoret (Marquis of), " Moise considéré comme législateur et comme moraliste." Paris, 1788. 8vo.

· " Guide for the Strayed."

Maïmoun (Moses ben) called Maimonides, " Le Guide des égarés, traité de théologie et de philosophie," published for the first time in the original Arabic and translated into French by S. Munk. Paris, 1856–1866. 3 vols., 8vo.

Page 2 of the manuscript.

CHRISTIANISM (Exegesis).

" History of the Christian Dogmas." Haag.

Haag (Eugène). " Histoire des Dogmes Chrétiens," 2nd edition. Paris, Cherbuliez, 1862. 2 vols., large 8vo.

" Notes for Ecclesiastical History." Tillemont (Le Nain de), " Mémoires pour servir à l'Histoire Ecclésiastique des six premiers siècles." Paris, 1693–1712. 16 vols., quarto.

" Studies on the Apocryphal Gospels." Michel Nicolas.

Nicolas (Michel). " Etudes sur les évangiles apocryphes." Paris, Lévy frères, 1865. 8vo.

" History of God."—Didron.

Didron Ainé. " Iconographie chrétienne. Histoire de Dieu." Paris, Didot frères, 1845, quarto. (Collection of unpublished documents on French history.)

" Symbols and Emblems."—Twining.

· Twining (Louisa). " Symbols and Emblems of Early Christian Art." London, Murray, 1852, quarto ; 500 illustrations.

· " Life of Jesus." " Apostles : St. Paul."—Renan.

Renan. " Histoire des origines du christianisme ; I. ' Vie de Jésus ' (Paris, 1863) ; II. ' Les Apôtres ' (Paris, 1866) ; ' Saint Paul ' " (Paris, 1869).

Article by Nefftzer on Bunsun's Bible.

Nefftzer published an article on the " Vollständiges Bibelwerk für die Gemeinde " of Chrn. Carl Josias Bunsen (Leipzic), 1858–1870. 9 vols., 8vo.

*) " St. Jérôme."—Amédée Thierry.

Thierry (Amédée). " Saint Jérôme, la société chrétienne
à Rome et l'émigration Romaine en Terre Sainte."
Paris, Didier & Coe, 1867. 2 vols., 8vo.

" The Apostles' Creed." M. Nicolas.

Nicolas (Michel). " Le Symbole des Apôtres, essai
historique." Paris, Lévy frères, 1867. 8vo.

" History of Christian Theology." Reuss.

Reuss (Edouard). " Histoire de la Théologie Chrétienne
au siècle apostolique," 3rd edition. Strasburg, 1864.
2 vols., 8vo.

" Eunapius." Victor Cousin.

Cousin (Victor). " Eunape, pour servir à l'histoire de la
philosophie d'Alexandrie." Paris, 1827. 8vo. (Extract
from the " Journal des savants," 1826 & 1827.)

" Critical History of the Alexandria School." Vacherot.

Vacherot (Etienne). " Histoire critique de l'école
d'Alexandrie." Paris, Ladrange, 1846–1851. 3 vols.,
8vo.

Iamblichus. " De Mysteriis."

Iamblichus. " De mysteriis Aegyptiorum." Venice,
1516. In folio.

" Eusebius, Socrates, Zozomenes, Theodoret." Cousin.

President Louis Cousin has published, in his " Histoire
de l'Eglise," the Life of Constantine, which is a translation from Eusebius of Caesarea, Socrates, Zozomenes,
Theodoret, &c. Paris, 1675.

" Evangelical Preparation." Eusebius.

Eusebius Pamphilius, " La Préparation Evangelique,"
translated from the Greek by Seguier de Saint-Brisson.
Paris, Gaume frères, 1846. 2 vols., 8vo.

" Historia Patriarcharum Alexandrinorum." Renaudot.

Renaudot (l'abbé Eusèbe). " Historia Patriarcharum
Alexandrinorum Jacobitarum a D. Marco. usque ad
finem saeculi XIII." Paris, 1713. 8vo.

" Statement of the Roman Catacombs." R. Rochette.

Rochette (Raoul). " Tableau des Catacombes de Rome

*) Compare both Saints

où l'on donne la description de ces cimetières sacrés."
Paris, 1837. 12mo.
" The Golden Legend."
Voragine (Jacques de). " La légende dorée en françois."
(Numerous editions in the XVth and XVIth centuries.)
Gibbon. Ch. XV.
Gibbon (Edward). " History of the Decline and Fall of
the Roman Empire," translated from the English. New
edition by Guizot. Vol. III., pp. 1–151. Paris, 1812.
The title of the XVth chapter is " The Progress of the
Christian Religion—Sentiments, Manners, Numbers and
Conditions of the Primitive Christians."
" Dictionary of Apocrypha."—Migne.
" Dictionnaire des Apocryphes ou Collection de tous les
livres apocryphes relatifs à l'Ancien et au Nouveau
Testament." Paris, Migne, 1856–1858. 2 vols., large 8vo.
This " Dictionnaire " forms the 23rd and 24th volumes of
" troisième et dernière Encyclopédie théologique," by
Abbé Migne.
" S. Irenaeus and the Gnostics." Réville. " Revue des
deux mondes."
Réville (Albert), Saint Irénée et les Gnostiques de son
temps, Revue des deux mondes, 1865. Vol. XV., p. 998–
1032.
" The Devil." Louandre, " Revue des deux mondes."
Charles Louandre published in the " Revue des deux
mondes " (August 15, 1842). " Le Diable, sa vie ses
mœurs, et son intervention dans les choses humaines."
" History of the Dogma of the Divinity of Jesus."
Réville.
Réville (Albert). " Histoire du Dogme de la Divinité de
Jésus Christ." Paris, 1868. 12mo.
" Tractatus theologico-politicus." Spinosa. *)
Spinosa. " Tractatus theologico-politicus." Hamburg,
1670. 4to.
Tertullian. " Apologetica."
There are numerous French translations of Tertullian's

*) Especially, opening pp. of Part III

"Apologetica." The most recent are that of M. de Genoude (1852), and that of the Abbé de Courcy (1857), &c.

Tertullian. "De Prescriptionibus."

Tertullian's "Prescriptions against Heretics" has been translated into French by Collombet (1845), by the Abbé de Courcy (1857), &c.

S. Nilus. "Treatise on the Deadly Sins."

S. Nilus, a monk, wrote a treatise on the deadly sins, which has been translated into Latin under the following title : "De octo spiritibus malitiæ." The works of S. Nilus form the 79th volume of the "Patrologie Grecque," by Abbé Migne.

Clement of Alexandria. "The Pedagogue."

"La Pédagogue est un excellent traité de morale divisé en trois livres." (Gallais, "Biographie Universelle," published by Michaud, in the article "Clément d'Alexandrie"); the works of Clement of Alexandria form the 8th and 9th volumes of the "Patrologie Grecque" by Abbé Migne.

"The Morality of the Church and the Morality of the Philosophers." Boutteville.

Boutteville (Lucien). "La Morale de l'Eglise et la morale naturelle, études critiques." Paris, Lévy frères, 1866. 8vo.

"Critical Examination of Doctrines." Larroque.

Larroque (Patrice). "Examen critique des doctrines de la religion chrétienne," 3rd edition, Paris, 1864. 2 vols., 8vo.

Manuscript note by Viollet-le-Duc on the basilica.

Page 3 of the manuscript.

D'Herbelot. Oriental Library.

D'Herbelot (Barthélemy). "Bibliothèque orientale, ou Dictionnaire universel, contenant généralement tout ce qui regarde la connaissance des peuples de l'Orient."

Posthumous work, put in order and published by Ant. Galland.   Paris, 1697, in fol.

Samuel Bochart.   " Hierozoicon."

Bochart (Samuel).   " Hierozoicon, sive de animalibus sacræ Scripturæ ; recensuit, suas notas adjecit," E. F. C. Rosenmuller, Leipzic, 1793–1796.   3 vols., quarto.

Physiologon.   " S. Epiphanes."

" Le Physiologue contient des réflexions morales relatives aux propriétés des animaux " (Cotteret, " Biographie universelle," published by Michaud in the article " S. Epiphane "). The works of S. Epiphanes form the 41st, 42nd, and 43rd volumes of Abbé Migne's " Patrologie grecque."

" History of Manichæanism."   Beausobre.

Beausobre (Isaac de).   " Histoire critique de Manichée et du Manichéisme."   Amsterdam, 1734–1739.   2 vols., quarto.

" Life of S. Anthony."   S. Athanasius.

Athanase (Saint).   " Vie de Saint Antoine," translated into French from the Greek by Manoury.   Paris, 1858. 12mo.

" The Life of S. Anthony."   Le Nain de Tillemont. Vols. VII. and VIII.

Tillemont (Le Nain de).   " Mémoires pour servir à l'histoire ecclésiastique des six premiers siècles."   Paris, 1693–1712.   16 vols., quarto.   Vol. VII. : " Histoires particulières depuis l'an 328 jusqu'en 371, hors Saint Athanase ; Tome VIII. : Vies de Saint Athanase et des saints morts depuis l'an 378 jusqu'en 394."

" The Desert Fathers."   Le Nain de Tillemont.   Vols. VII. and VIII.

Tillemont (Le Nain de).   " Mémoires," &c.

" S. Theresa."   Her life.

" Vie de Sainte Thérèse, écrite par elle même," translated into French by Arnaud d'Andilly.   Avignon, 1828.

S. Theresa.   " The Castle of the Soul."

S. Thérèse. " Le Chasteau de l'âme," translated into French by Arnaud d'Andilly. Avignon, 1828.

Mme. Guyon. " The Torrents."

Guyon (Mme). " Opuscules spirituels," Cologne, 1704. 12mo. The treatise on " Torrents " (of the spirit) was printed for the first time in these " opuscules."

" Buddhism " (Introduction to the history of). Burnouf.

Burnouf (Eugène). " Introduction à l'histoire du Bouddhisme indien." Paris, Imprimerie Royale, 1845. 4to.

" The Lotus of the Excellent Law." Burnouf.

Burnouf (Eugène). " Le Lotus de la bonne loi," translated from the Sanscrit, accompanied by a commentary and twenty-one notes relative to Buddhism. Paris, Imprimerie Nationale, 1852. 4to.

" Lalitavistara." Foucaux.

Foucaux (Philippe-Edouard). " Rgya tch'er rol pa, ou Développement des jeux, contenant l'histoire du Bouddha Cakya Mouni," translated from the Thibetan version of the bkah Hgyour, and revised with the original Sanscrit (Lalitavistara), by Ph.E. Foucaux. Paris, 1848–1849. 2 vols., 4to.

Cicero. " Philosophical Works."

Cicéron. " Oeuvres Philosophiques." Paris, Imprimerie Didot, Jeune 1795. 10 vols., 18mo. This collection, published by Bozérian, and consisting of old translations, does not contain the Latin text.

Plato. " Phaedo ; Phaedrus ; the Symposium ; Meno ; Timaeus ; Critias."

Platon. " Oeuvres," translated from the Greek by Victor Cousin. Paris, 1826–1835. 10 vols., 8vo.

" The Dream of Scipio."

Cicéron. " Le Songe de Scipion " (fragment of the VIth book of " The Republic "), translated into French by Abbé J. B. Geoffroy. Paris, 1725. 12mo.

" Heaven and Earth." Reynaud.

Reynaud (Jean). " Terre et ciel. Philosophie religieuse," 4th edition. Paris, 1864. 8vo.

PHILOSOPHY.

"History of the Moral Ideas of Antiquity." Denis.
Denis (Jacques). "Histoire des théories et des Idées
Morales dans l'Antiquité." Paris, 1856. 2 vols., 8vo.
. Spinosa. "Saisset."
Spinosa. "Oeuvres," translated by Emile Saisset. New
edition, Paris, 1861. 3 vols., 12mo.
. Plotinus. "The Ennéades." Bouillet.
Plotin. "Les Ennéades," translated into French by
N. Bouillet. Paris, 1857–1861. 3 vols., 8vo.
. Renouvier. "Manual of Ancient Philosophy."
Renouvier (Charles). "Manuel de Philosophie An-
cienne." Paris, 1844. 2 vols., 12mo.
. Renouvier. Manual of Modern Philosophy.
Renouvier (Charles). "Manuel de Philosophie Moderne."
Paris, 1842. 12mo.
. S. Augustine. "The City of God."
Augustin (Saint). "La Cité de Dieu." New translation
by Emile Saisset. Paris, 1855. 4 vols., 12mo. Other
translations by Lombert, Goujet, Moreau, &c.
. Kant. "Critique of Pure Reason." Barni.
Flaubert made an error in attributing the translation of
Kant's "Critique of Pure Reason" to Barni. It is by
Tissot (3rd edition, Paris, 1864, 2 vols., 8vo). Barni
translated the "Critique of Practical Reason" from the
German (Paris, 1848, 8vo), and the "Critique of Judg-
ment," both by Kant (Paris, 1846, 2 vols., 8vo).
. "S. Martin." Franck.
Franck (Adolphe). "Dictionnaire des Sciences Philoso-
phiques," Vol. IV., pp. 125–130, article, "Martin"
(Louis-Claude de Saint-). Paris, 1849.

HERESIES.

. "Apollonius of Tyana." Chassang.
Chassang (Alexis). "Apollonius de Tyane, sa vie, ses
voyages, ses prodiges," by Philostratus, and his letters;

Q

translated from the Greek by A. Chassang. Paris, 1862. 8vo.

. "The Recognitions of S. Clement."
S. Clement, the companion of S. Paul, was the second or third successor of S. Peter to the see of Rome. Various writings are attributed to him, mentioned by Fabricius (Bibliotheca Graeca editio nova, Vol. VII. and sqq. Hamburg, 1801). "Toute la littérature pseudo-Clémentine—Homélies, Récognitions, &c., est une œuvre apochryphe ou romanesque," says Abbé Vigouroux ("Dictionnaire de la Bible," Vol. II., col. 803. Paris, 1899).

. "Grabbe's Spicilegium, for Simon (Magus)."
Grabius (Joan.-Ernestus). "Spicilegium SS. Patrum, ut et hæreticorum sæculi post Christum natum 1, 2, et 3, editio auctior, Oxonii," 1724. 2 vols., 8vo.

. "History of Gnosticism." Matter.
Matter (Jacques). "Histoire critique du Gnosticisme et de son influence sur les sectes religieuses et philosophiques des six premiers siècles de l'ère chrétienne," 2nd edition. Strasburg, 1843–1844. 3 vols., 8vo.

"S. Epiphanes."
"Divi Epiphanii episcopi Constantiæ Cypri, Contra octoginta hæreses opus eximium." Basle, 1544, in fol.

"De hæresibus." S. Augustine.
Augustinus (Sanctus). "Opera omnia, emendata opera et studio monachorum ordinis sancti Benedicti e congregatione S. Mauri. Editio parisina altera." Vol. VIII. pars I., col. 33–68: "De Hæresibus ad Quodvultdeum liber unus." (Paris, 1837.)

Pluquet.
Pluquet (l'abbé). "Mémoires pour servir à l'histoire des égarements de l'esprit humain par rapport à la religion chrétienne, ou Dictionnaire des hérésies, des erreurs, et des schismes." Paris, 1762. 2 vols., 8vo. This work was reprinted under the following title: "Dictionnaire des hérésies, des erreurs, et des schismes."

Page 4 of the manuscript.

Bayle. " Article on the Manichaeans."

Bayle. " Dictionnaire historique et critique," 3rd edition. Rotterdam, 1720. 4 vols., in fol. There are several editions of this " Dictionnaire," to which Flaubert refers for the article " Manichéens."

Salvador. " Jesus and His Doctrine."

Salvador (Joseph). " Jésus Christ et sa doctrine : histoire de la naissance de l'Eglise et de ses progrès pendant le premier siècle." New edition. Paris, Lévy frères, 1864–1865. 2 vols., 8vo.

" Life of Jesus." Strauss.

Strauss (David-Frédéric). " Vie de Jésus, ou examen critique de son histoire," translated from the German by E. Littré, 3rd edition in French. Paris, 1864. 2 vols., 8vo.

Voltaire. " Theological Questions."

Voltaire published : (1) " Questions de Zapata " ; (2) " Questions proposées à qui voudra les résoudre " ; (3) " Questions sur l'Encyclopédie " ; (4) " Questions (ou lettres) sur les miracles."

Fleury. " Ecclesiastical History."

Fleury (L'Abbé). " Histoire ecclésiastique depuis la naissance de Jésus-Christ." Paris, 1691. 36 vols., 4to.

S. Augustine. " Faith, Hope, and Charity."

Augustinus (Sanctus). " Opera omnia. Editio parisina altera," Vol. VI., pars. I., col. 333–410 : Enchiridion ad Laurentium, sive de fide, spe et charitate liber unus (Paris, 1837).

Aelian. " Animals."

Aeliani. " De animalium natura, libri XVII., græce et latine." London, 1744. 2 vols., 4to.

Aelian. " Various Stories."

Aeliani. " Variae Historiae, libri XIV." Rome, 1545. 4to.

Pliny.

Plinius secundus (Caius). "Naturalis historiae, libri XXXVII." (Several editions.)

MYTHOLOGY.

Lucian.
Luciani. "Opera, græce et latine." Paris, F. Didot, 1840. Large 8vo.
Pausanias.
Pausanias. "Description de la Grèce." New translation, with the Greek text, by Et. Clavier. Paris, 1814–1823. 7 vols., 8vo.
Macrobius.
"Les œuvres de Macrobe." New translation, with the Latin text. Paris, 1845–1847. 3 vols., 8vo.
Aulus Gellius.
Aulu-Gelle. "Les nuits Attiques." New translation, with the Latin text. Paris, 1845–1847. 3 vols., 8vo.
Apuleius.
Apulée. "Oeuvres." New translation by V. Bétolaud. Paris, 1835–1836. 4 vols., 8vo.
Creuzer.
Creuzer (G.-Fr.). "Les religions de l'antiquité, consi- dérées principalement dans leurs formes symboliques et mythologiques." Translated from the German by J. D. Guigniaut. Paris, Didot frères. 4 vols., 8vo, in 10 parts.
Ménard. "Morality before the Philosophers."
Ménard (Louis). "De la Morale avant les Philosophes." Paris, 1860. 8vo. (Thesis presented to the "Faculté des lettres" of Paris.)
Preller. "Roman Mythology."
Preller (Ludwig). "Les Dieux de l'ancienne Rome; Mythologie Romaine." Translated from the German by L. Dietz, with a preface by Alfred Maury. Paris, Didier et Cie, 1865. 8vo.
Gibbon. "From Commodus to Julian."
Gibbon. "History of the Decline and Fall of the

Roman Empire," translated from the English. New edition by Guizot. Paris, 1812. 13 vols., 8vo.
Procopius. "Secret History."
'Ανέκδοτα or "Histoire Secrète de Justinien," by the senator Procopius of Cæsarea, translated by Isambert. Paris, 1856. 8vo. Gibbon speaks of Procopius and his writings in Vol. VII. (pp. 222, sqq.) of his "History of the Decline of the Roman Empire" (new edition by Guizot).
"Historia Orientalis." Hottinger.
Hottinger (J. H.). "Historia Orientalis, ex variis orientalibus monumentis collecta." Zurich, 1652. 4to.
"Magic and Astrology in Antiquity." Maury.
Maury (Alfred). "La magie et l'Astrologie dans l'Antiquité et au moyen âge, ou étude sur les superstitions païennes qui se sont perpétuées jusqu'à nos jours." Paris, 1860. 4to.
"Demons." Extracts from the "City of God." Saisset, Augustin (Saint). "La Cité de Dieu." New translation, with an introduction and notes by Emile Saisset. Paris, 1855. 4 vols., 12mo.

[RED NOTE-BOOK.]
Petri Gyllii. "De topographia Constantinopolis."
Gyllius (Petrus). "De Bosphoro Thracio, libri III., et de topographia Constantinopoleos et de illius antiquitatibus, libri IV." Lyons, 1561. 4to. The third volume of the "Collection des chroniques nationales françaises" (Paris, 1828) contains (pp. 293–321) an extract from this book, under the following title : "Description du Bosphore et de la ville de Constantinople," translated from the Greek of Pierre Gilles, by the Comte d'Hauterive.
"Contorniate Medallions." Sabatier.
Sabatier (J.). "Description générale des Médaillons contorniates." Paris, 1860–1861. 4to, with 18 plates.
Panvinius. "Ludi Circenses."
Panvinius (Onuphrius). "De ludis circensibus, libri II., de triumphis, liber unus." Patavii, 1861, in fol.

Rougé. " Studies on Funeral Ritual."

Rougé (Vicomte Emmanuel de). " Rituel Funéraire des anciens Egyptiens." Paris, 1861–1868, in fol.

Tertullian. Réville, " Revue de Théologie," 1853.

Albert Réville also published in the " Revue des deux mondes " (1864, Vol. LIV., pp. 166–199) : " Tertullien et le montanisme."

Tholuck. " Sufismus."

Tholuck (F. A. D.). " Sufismus sive theosophia Persarum pantheistica, quam e MSS. Bibliothecae regiae Berolinensis persicis, arabicis, turcisis eruit et illustravit." Berlin, 1821. 8vo.

Manès. " Foucher, mém. de l'Acad. des Inscriptions." Foucher (l'abbé). Sequel to the " Traité historique de la religion des Perses." Second period. Eighth note : " Système de Manès " (" Histoire de l'Academie royale des inscriptions et belles-lettres," Vol. XXXI., pp. 443–479. Paris, 1768).

" Commercial Relations between the Roman Empire and Asia." Reinaud.

Reinaud (J. T.). " Relations politiques et commerciales de l'Empire Romain avec l'Asie orientale (l'Hyrcanie, l'Inde, la Bactriane et la Chine) pendant les cinq premiers siècles de l'ère chrétienne, d'après les témoignages latins, grecs, arabes, persans, indiens, et chinois." Paris, 1863. 8vo.

" Destruction of Paganism." Chastel.

Chastel (Etienne-Louis). " Histoire de la Destruction du Paganisme dans l'empire d'Orient." Geneva, 1850. 8vo.

" Testament of Adam." Renan. " Journal Asiatique."

Renan (Ernest). Fragments of the gnostic book entitled " Apocalypse d'Adam," or " Pénitence d'Adam," or " Testament d'Adam," after two Syriac versions (" Journal Asiatique," 5th series, Vol. II., 1853, pp. 427–471).

" Monastic Life of the Hindoos." Bochinger.

. Bochinger (J. J.). " La vie contemplative, ascétique et monastique chez les Indous et chez les peuples bouddhistes." Strasburg, 1831, in fol.

. " Historical Researches on Madness." Trélat.
Trélat (Ulysse). " Recherches Historiques sur la Folie." Paris, 1839. 8vo.

. Goerres. " Mysticism."
Goerres (Jean-Joseph de). " La mystique divine, naturelle et diabolique." Translated from the German by Charles Sainte-Foi. Second edition. Paris, 1862. 5 vols., 12mo.

. " Mental Maladies." Esquirol.
. Esquirol (J. E. D.). " Des maladies mentales, considérées sous les rapports médical, hygiénique et médico-légal." Paris, 1838. 2 vols., 8vo, and atlas.

Palladii. " Lausiaca Historia."
Palladii. " Historia Lausiaca SS. patrum qui vitam degebant in solitudine, graece, cum notis latinis Jo. Meursii." Lugduni Batavorum, 1616. 4to. This book has also been entitled : " Historia Lausiaca, sive vita monachorum, ad Lausum praefectum."

. " De forma Christi." Vavasseur.
Vavasseur (le P. Francois). " De forma Christi liber." Paris, 1649. 8vo.

. " Revelations of S. Pacomius." Dulaurier.
Dulaurier (Edouard). " Fragments des révélations apocryphes de saint Barthélemy et de l'histoire des communautés religieuses fondées par saint Pacome, traduits sur les textes coptes-thébains inédits, conservés à la Bibliothèque du Roi." Paris, 1835. 8vo.

FINIS

t. Anthony, b. in Egypt c. 250 A.D. Withdrew from the
world c. 270. For 15 yrs. lived alone in a hut
near his home. Then for 20 yrs in remote
solitude in a desert. His fame spread.
Multitudes came to hear him preach.
Accordingly, about 305 he came forth to teach,
to encourage an hermit's life. He practiced
extreme austerities, reducing food, drink,
sleep to a minim. The devil constantly
assailed him with lustful visions. By the end
of his life, the Thebaid (the desert near
Egyptian Thebes) was full of hermits
inspired by his example + precepts.
Died in 350 A.D. He was the first Christian monk